Folens

Essential
Fiction Genres

Models for Writing

Peter Ellison

United Kingdom: Folens Publishers, Apex Business Centre, Boscombe Road, Dunstable, LU5 4RL.
Email: folens@folens.com

Ireland: Folens Publishers, Greenhills Road, Tallaght, Dublin 24.
Email: info@folens.ie

Poland: JUKA, ul. Renesansowa 38, Warsaw 01-905.

Editor: Emma Thomas
Design and layout: 2idesign ltd, Cambridge
Cover design: 2idesign ltd, Cambridge

First published 2003 by Folens Limited.

British Library Cataloguing in Publication Data. A catalogue record for this publication is available from the British Library.

ISBN 1 84303 381 X

Acknowledgements

Thanks to Jacob for all the reading and advice.

Text extracts: Extract taken from SIR GAWAIN AND THE GREEN KNIGHT Text © 1981 Selina Hastings. Illustrated by Juan Wijngaard. Reproduced by permission of Walker Books Ltd., London. *Guards! Guards!* by Terry Pratchett (Victor Gollancz, 1989). *The Lord of the Rings* by J.R.R. Tolkien (HarperCollins, 1954) Copyright © J.R.R. Tolkien, 1954. Reprinted by permission of HarperCollins Publishers Ltd. 1552 words from ARTEMIS FOWL by Eoin Colfer (Viking, 2001). © Eoin Colfer, 2001. *Blood Feud* by Rosemary Sutcliff (Puffin,1978). Reproduced by permission of David Higham Associates. 'London Rises from the Ashes (and how it nearly all went wrong)' by Jeremy Strong from *A Century of Stories* edited by Wendy Cooling (HarperCollins, 1999). Reproduced by permission of David Higham Associates. THE RUBY IN THE SMOKE by Philip Pullman, copyright © Philip Pullman, 1985. Reproduced by permission of Scholastic Ltd. *The War of the Worlds* by H.G. Wells (Heinemann, 1898). Reproduced by permission of A.P. Watt Ltd on behalf of the Literary Executors of the Estate of H.G. Wells. Extract taken from MAPHEAD © 1994 Lesley Howarth. Reproduced by permission of Walker Books Ltd., London. *They're Made Out of Meat* by Terry Bisson, URL: http://www.terrybisson.com/index.html. Reproduced by permission of the author. *Bloodtide* by Melvyn Burgess (Andersen Press, 1999). Reproduced by permission of Andersen Press. *A Daughter, Lost* by Pam McNew. Copyright © Pam McNew, 2002. All Rights Reserved. Reproduced by permission of the author. URL: http://www.chizine.com/daughterlostp.htm. *The Flowers* by Alice Walker (The Women's Press, 2000). *Kiss and Tell* by Cherry Adair (Ivy, 2000). *Bridget Jones's Diary* by Helen Fielding (Picador, 1996). Reproduced by permission of Macmillan, London, UK. *The Big Sleep* by Raymond Chandler (Hamish Hamilton, 1939). Extract from BUCKET NUT Copyright © Liza Cody 1992. Reproduced by permission of Felicity Bryan and the author.

Photographs and Illustrations: Cover Image: The Kobal Collection / New Line / Saul Zaentz / Wing Nut / Vinet, Pierre; page 7 The Kobal Collection / New Line / Saul Zaentz / Wing Nut; pages 8–11 'Doune Castle', © CROWN COPYRIGHT REPRODUCED COURTESY OF HISTORIC SCOTLAND; page 12 'The Grim Reaper' Masterfile; page 16 'The Lord of the Rings: The Fellowship of the Ring' Copyright 2001, New Line Productions, Inc. TM The Saul Zaentz Company d/b/a Tolkien Enterprises under license to New Line Productions, Inc. All rights reserved. Photo by Pierre Vinet. Photo appears courtesy of New Line Productions, Inc.; page 18 'Illustration by John Howe' © John Howe, 2001 from *The Lord of the Rings Official Movie Guide* by Brian Sibley. Reprinted by permission of HarperCollins Publishers Ltd; page 20–21 JORGEN SCHYTTE / Still pictures; page 25 'Replica of Sutton Hoo Helmet', © The British Museum; pages 26–31 'Viking Warrior' © The York Archaeological Trust; page 69 Adri Berger / Getty Images; page 94 The Kobal Collection / Working Title / Bailey, Alex; page 99 Steve Prezant / Corbis; page 109 THE KOBAL COLLECTION / WARNER BROS; pages 114–115 Digital Vision; page 118 Ghislain & Marie David de Lossy / Getty Images.

Contents

Contents

Introduction

Essential Fiction Genres

I know all about fiction. That just means 'stories' doesn't it?

Yes – 'fiction' refers to something 'made-up' or imagined, but that's not the whole picture. As you know, there are many different genres of story, such as fantasy, science fiction, horror, and so on. But are you aware how these have changed over time? Could you find connections between them? And could you pick out the key elements that make them so exciting or powerful to read?

What's so essential about these stories?

The texts have been carefully chosen to present the best examples of genre fiction – and to show you how professional writers do it.

Why does it have that other title – 'Models for Writing'?

Well, although you will read each text first, the point of the book is to help you learn about techniques good writers use in order to express their ideas, or entertain their readers. In other words, to provide you with models that you can imitate. Stories aren't just about good beginnings, middles and ends – although they help!

How will the book help me? I don't know what these key techniques are.

The book is divided into six sections. Each section focuses on specific aspects of genre writing, such as recreating the past. In addition, the grouping of texts together will help you make comparisons and note contrasts between them, and see how some writers deal with the same idea or issue.

In addition, every single text is preceded by a section called 'About the text'. This asks you to look out for key features, at Word, Sentence and Text level, as you read. In this way, the key features will become clear to you.

Sounds good, but why should I take this seriously?

The author is Peter Ellison, an experienced English teacher and educational writer. He has also worked closely with exam boards at GCSE level, so he knows about assessment requirements too. He is very well placed to give you advice, and provide you with interesting and wide-ranging examples of texts.

Ultimately, you should read the texts to enjoy them yourself. However, through your reading and study of them, you will improve your writing skills. This will be of benefit to all your school work, and will prepare you for examinations and other forms of assessment. Above all, the book will show you how professional storytellers work, and how you can write in the way they do.

Imagined worlds

About the chapter

Many of the first stories ever told were probably what we now call tales of 'fantasy'. In this chapter, you will read the opening of one of the oldest stories written in English and an extract from one of the most popular books ever written, as well as examples of exciting contemporary fantasy writing.

As you read, consider the idea that reading fantasy fiction enables us to live through experiences that we could never otherwise encounter.

fantasy

About the text

This is a modern re-telling of *Sir Gawain and the Green Knight* by Selina Hastings. The earliest written version of this legend dates from the late fourteenth century but it may be even older. It is Christmas in King Arthur's court at Camelot. The festivities are in full swing when a monstrous stranger interrupts.

As you read, consider the following features of the text:

Word level

- Are there any words that immediately tell the reader that the story is set in medieval times?

Sentence level

- Look at the narrative (how the story is told) and the way the characters speak. Can you tell that the original was written in an older form of English? Find some examples of old-fashioned sentence style.

- Look closely at the sentence beginning, *Hardly had he spoken …* . This is a very long sentence in a crucial part of the story. Examine its construction. Would a series of shorter sentences be as effective?

Text level

- This is the opening of the story. How does the writer set the scene and prepare us for the surprise entrance?

- How does the final paragraph of this extract prepare the reader for the rest of the story?

- The events in the rest of the story test Gawain's bravery and honesty. How do you think the story will develop?

fantasy

Sir Gawain and the Green Knight

by Selina Hastings

IT WAS CHRISTMAS, and King Arthur and his knights of the Round Table were at Camelot. For a full fifteen days there had been feasting and jousting, music and dancing. On the first day of the New Year, the King himself led the dance with Guinevere his Queen. At dinner, according to custom, he insisted that everyone be served before he would sit down. He announced that he would not eat until he had heard some tale of great adventure.

Hardly had he spoken, his voice clear above the talking and laughter and sound of trumpets, when there rode into the hall a terrifying figure – a giant of a man, massively built, whose vast limbs, even his hair and beard, were a brilliant green. He wore a green tunic and from his shoulders hung a richly embroidered cloak trimmed with green fur. The saddle and bridle of his horse were of green leather studded with emeralds, its mane and tail plaited with green silk. Holding in one hand a branch of holly and in the other a huge axe, the green giant rode up to the banqueting table. 'Which of you is the King?' he demanded. Nobody moved. The entire company was speechless with astonishment at this unearthly apparition.

Arthur was the first to recover. 'I am the King,' he said courteously. 'And I invite you to join our feast.'

'I cannot stay,' replied the Knight. 'I have come to challenge you and your knights – by repute the bravest men in **Christendom**. Is there any man bold enough to exchange blows with me?'

> **Christendom** the Christian world

setting the scene, introducing a problem **9**

He paused for a moment, then continued. 'The rules are that he aim a blow at me now with this axe. In exactly one year's time he must allow me to return that blow.'

No-one spoke. The Knight looked around, surprised. 'What!' he exclaimed. 'Are these the famous knights of the Round Table, and not one of you dares give me an answer?'

Arthur, stung by the contempt in the stranger's voice, leaped to his feet. 'The game you propose is foolish,' he said. 'But I will take you on. Give me your axe.'

Then Gawain, the youngest of the knights, stood up. 'Sire, please let me take up this challenge. I have not yet had a chance to prove myself. I beg you to grant me this favour.'

'Noble Gawain,' replied Arthur, 'take the axe. Strike your blow boldly.'

'A noble opponent indeed!' exclaimed the Green Knight, dismounting from his horse. 'Sir Gawain, you must swear that

in exactly one year and a day you will seek me out and allow me to return your blow.'

'I give you my word,' said Gawain. Then the Green Knight knelt at Gawain's feet, bowing his head so that his neck was plainly exposed. Gawain lifted the axe up high and brought it whistling down, severing the Knight's head cleanly from his shoulders.

The head rolled on the floor, blood spurting from the wound, but the Knight never faltered. Rising to his feet, he picked up his head and, tucking it under his arm, swung himself into the saddle.

As he passed Gawain, the head turned and regarded him solemnly. 'Remember your promise, Gawain. Meet me at the Green Chapel in one year and a day.' Then, spurring his horse, the Green Knight galloped out of the hall.

setting the scene, introducing a problem

About the text

Terry Pratchett is widely regarded as the master of comic fantasy. His *Discworld* novels have sold in their millions worldwide and he has also written award-winning books for younger readers.

In this extract from *Guards! Guards!*, we join Zebbo Mooty in the dangerous streets of Discworld's capital, Ankh-Morpok.

As you read, consider the following features of the text:

Word level

- Notice how Terry Pratchett mixes formal and informal language for comic effect.

- The Grim Reaper speaks in capital letters. What effect does this create?

Sentence level

- Look closely at the paragraph beginning, *He was the first ...* . See how Terry Pratchett varies the length and structure of the sentences so that he delays giving the reader the information that Zebbo is dead. Try removing *however*. What effect does this have?

Text level

- How does the author make Zebbo's death funny while still encouraging the reader to feel sympathy for him?

- Look at the difference between the ways Zebbo and Death speak.

- Notice that Terry Pratchett does not describe the dragon. Why do you think this is?

Guards! Guards!

by Terry Pratchett

It was about to be the worst night of his life for Zebbo Mooty, Thief Third Class, and it wouldn't have made him any happier to know that it was also going to be the last one. The rain was keeping people indoors, and he was way behind on his quota. He was, therefore, a little less cautious than he might otherwise have been.

In the night time streets of Ankh-Morpok caution is an absolute. There is no such thing as moderately cautious. You are either very cautious, or you are dead. You might be walking around and breathing, but you're dead, just the same.

He heard the muffled sounds coming from the nearby alley, slid his leather-bound **cosh** from his sleeve, waited until the victim was almost turning the corner, sprang out, said 'Oh, shi—' and died.

It was a most unusual death. No-one else had died like that for hundreds of years.

cosh thick, heavy stick used as a weapon

The stone wall behind him glowed cherry red with heat, which gradually faded into darkness.

He was the first to see the Ankh–Morpok dragon. He derived little comfort from knowing this, however, because he was dead.

'–t,' he said, and his disembodied self looked down at the small heap of charcoal which, he knew with an unfamiliar sort of certainty, was what he had just been disembodied from. It was a strange sensation, seeing your own mortal remains. He didn't find it as horrifying as he would have imagined if you'd asked him, say, ten minutes ago. Finding that you are dead is **mitigated** by also finding that there really is a *you* who can find you dead.

The alley opposite was empty again.

'That was really strange,' said Mooty.

EXTREMELY UNUSUAL, CERTAINLY.

'Did you see that? What was it?' Mooty looked up at the dark figure emerging from the shadows. 'Who're you anyway?' he added suspiciously.

GUESS, said the voice.

Mooty peered at the hooded figure.

'Cor!' he said. 'I thought you dint turn up for the likes o' me.'

I TURN UP FOR *EVERYONE*.

'I mean in ... person, sort of thing.'

SOMETIMES. ON SPECIAL OCCASIONS.

'Yeah, well,' said Mooty, 'this is one of them, all right! I mean, it looked like a bloody dragon! What's a man to do? You don't expect to find a dragon around the corner!'

AND NOW, IF YOU WOULD CARE TO STEP THIS WAY ... said Death, laying a skeletal hand on Mooty's shoulder.

'Do you know, a fortune teller once told me I'd die in bed, surrounded by grieving great-grandchildren,' said Mooty, following the stately figure. 'What do you think of that, eh?'

I THINK SHE WAS WRONG.

'A bloody dragon,' said Mooty. 'Fire breathing, too. Did I suffer much?'

NO. IT WAS PRACTICALLY INSTANTANEOUS.

'That's good. I wouldn't like to think I'd suffered much.' Mooty looked around him. 'What happens now?' he said.

Behind them, the rain washed the little heap of black ash into the mud.

About the text

Frodo Baggins, a hobbit from the Shire, finds himself in possession of a ring that has magical powers. To prevent it getting into the hands of the evil Sauron, Frodo and his hobbit friends leave the safety of their homes and take their chances in unknown and dangerous lands. In this extract, Frodo becomes separated from his friends and lost in the darkness.

As you read, consider the following features of the text:

Word level

- Look at the adjectives and adverbs in the passage. How do they help to create tension and fear? (Why *wholly dark* instead of just *dark*?)

- Tolkien has invented *Barrow-wights*. Why doesn't he explain what they are?

Sentence level

- How does Tolkien use the structure of his sentences to convey Frodo's nervousness and fear? Do you notice any changes in sentence length and structure during the passage?

Text level

- How does the physical description help to build tension at the beginning of the extract?

- How does the text change after *and he remembered no more*?

- How does Tolkien move from the specific description of Frodo to general comments about hobbits? Look at the paragraph beginning, *But though his fear was so great that it seemed to be …* .

- At the end of the extract, how does Tolkien reveal the awful situation? Look at the section starting, *He turned, and there in the cold glow …* .

fantasy

THE Lord OF THE Rings

by J.R.R. Tolkien

From some way off, or so it seemed, he thought he heard a cry: 'Hoy! Frodo! Hoy!' It was away eastward, on his left as he stood under the great stones, staring and straining into the gloom. He plunged off in the direction of the call, and found himself going steeply uphill.

As he struggled on he called again, and kept on calling more and more frantically; but he heard no answer for some time, and then it seemed faint and far ahead and high above him. 'Frodo! Hoy!' came the thin voices out of the mist: and then a cry that sounded like *help, help!* often repeated, ending with a last *help!* that trailed off into a long wail suddenly cut short. He stumbled forward with all the speed he could towards the cries; but the light was now gone, and clinging night had closed about him, so that it was impossible to be sure of any direction. He seemed all the time to be climbing up and up.

Only the change in the level of the ground at his feet told him when he at last came to the top of a ridge or hill. He was weary, sweating and yet chilled. It was wholly dark.

'Where are you?' he cried out miserably.

There was no reply. He stood listening. He was suddenly aware that it was getting very cold, and that up here a wind was beginning to blow, an icy wind. A change was coming in the weather. The mist was flowing past him now in shreds and tatters. His breath was smoking, and the darkness was less near and thick. He looked up and saw with surprise that faint stars were appearing overhead amid the strands of hurrying cloud and fog. The wind began to hiss over the grass.

He imagined suddenly that he caught a muffled cry, and he made towards it; and even as he went forward the mist was rolled up and thrust aside, and the starry sky was unveiled. A glance showed him that he was now facing southwards and was on a round hill-top, which he must have climbed from the north. Out of the east the biting wind was blowing.

To his right there loomed against the westward stars a dark black shape. A great **barrow** stood there.

'Where are you?' He cried again, both angry and afraid.

'Here!' said a voice, deep and cold, that seemed to come out of the ground. 'I am waiting for you!'

'No!' said Frodo; but he did not run away. His knees gave, and he fell on the ground. Nothing happened, and there was no sound. Trembling he looked up, in time to see a tall dark figure like a shadow against the stars. It leaned over him. He thought there were two eyes, very cold though lit with a pale light that seemed to come from some remote distance. Then a grip stronger and colder than iron seized him. The icy

Frodo confronts the Black Riders at the Ford of Bruinen later in the story.

fantasy

touch froze his bones, and he remembered no more.

wight an old English word for thing or creature

When he came to himself again, for a moment he could recall nothing except a sense of dread. Then suddenly he knew that he was imprisoned, caught hopelessly; he was in a barrow. A Barrow-**wight** had taken him, and he was probably already under the dreadful spells of the Barrow-wights about which whispered tales spoke. He dared not move, but lay as he found himself: flat on his back upon a cold stone with his hands on his breast.

But though his fear was so great that it seemed to be part of the very darkness that was round him, he found himself as he lay thinking about Bilbo Baggins and his stories, of their jogging along together in the lanes of the Shire and talking about roads and adventures. There is a seed of courage hidden (often deeply, it is true) in

the heart of the fattest and most timid hobbit, waiting for some final and desperate danger to make it grow. Frodo was neither very fat nor very timid; indeed, though he did not know it, Bilbo (and Gandalf) had thought him the best hobbit in the Shire. He thought he had come to the end of his adventure, and a terrible end, but the thought hardened him. He found himself stiffening, as if for a final spring; he no longer felt limp like a helpless prey.

As he lay there, thinking and getting a hold of himself, he noticed all at once that the darkness was slowly giving way: a pale greenish light was growing round him. It did not at first show him what kind of a place he was in, for the light seemed to be coming out of himself, and from the floor beside him, and had not yet reached the roof or wall. He turned, and there in the cold glow he saw lying beside him Sam, Pippin, and Merry. They were on their backs, and their faces looked deathly pale; and they were clad in white. About them lay many treasures, of gold maybe, though in that light they looked cold and unlovely. On their heads were circlets, gold chains were about their waists, and on their fingers were many rings. Swords lay by their sides, and shields were at their feet. But across their three necks lay one long naked sword.

About the text

Twelve-year-old Artemis Fowl is a brilliant criminal mastermind determined to make himself rich with fairy gold.

In this extract, Artemis and his manservant Butler are tracking down *The Book*, which will give Artemis power over the fairy world. A tip-off leads him to Ho Chi Minh City in Vietnam where his informant, Nguyen, takes him to a dark corner of the city.

As you read, consider the following features of the text:

Word level

- Artemis has a very precise way of speaking. What does this tell us about his character? How does it contrast with the way the fairy speaks?

Sentence level

- The paragraph beginning, *They climbed down from the vehicle ...* on this page is threatening and violent. How does Eoin Colfer use sentence structure and word choice to create this tone?

- Look at the sentence that describes Butler breaking the pickpocket's fingers. Try re-writing it to make it more emotional.

Text level

- What impression do we get of Artemis from this passage? How is this impression created?

- Look at the way Eoin Colfer integrates description and narration into the dialogue.

- He also includes a great deal of information about fairies throughout the passage.

The jeep could go only so far. Eventually the side streets grew too narrow for the four-wheel drive. Artemis turned to Nguyen. 'It seems we must proceed on foot, Mister Nguyen. Run if you like, but expect a sharp and fatal pain between your shoulder blades.'

Nguyen glanced into Butler's eyes. They were a deep blue, almost black. There was no mercy in those eyes. 'Don't worry,' he said. 'I won't run.'

They climbed down from the vehicle. A thousand suspicious eyes followed their progress along the steaming alley. An unfortunate pickpocket

Artemis Fowl
by Eoin Colfer

attempted to steal Butler's wallet. The manservant broke the man's fingers without looking down. They were given a wide berth after that.

The alley narrowed to a rutted lane. Sewage and drainpipes fed directly on to the muddy surface. Cripples and beggars huddled on rice-mat islands. Most of the residents of this lane had nothing to spare, with the exception of three.

'Well?' demanded Artemis. 'Where is she?'

Nguyen jabbed a finger towards a black triangle beneath a rusted fire escape.

'There. Under there. She never comes out. Even to buy rice spirits, she sends a runner. Now, can I go?'

Artemis didn't bother answering. Instead he picked his way across the puddled lane to the lee of the fire escape. He could discern furtive movements in the shadows.

'Butler, could you hand me the goggles?'

Butler plucked a set of night-vision glasses from his belt and placed them in Artemis's outstretched hand. The focus motor buzzed to suit the light.

Artemis fixed the glasses to his face. Everything became radioactive green. Taking a deep breath, he turned his gaze to the squirming shadows. Something squatted on a raffia mat, shifting uneasily in the almost non-existent light. Artemis fine-tuned the focus. The figure was small, abnormally so, and wrapped in a filthy shawl. Empty spirit jugs were half-buried in the mud around her. One forearm poked from the material. It seemed green. But then, so did everything else.

'Madam,' he said, 'I have a proposition for you.'

The figure's head wobbled sleepily.

'Wine,' she rasped, her voice like nails on a school board. 'Wine, English.'

Artemis smiled. The **gift of tongues**, aversion to light. Check, check.

'Irish, actually. Now, about my proposition?'

The healer shook a bony finger craftily. 'Wine first. Then talk.'

'Butler?'

The bodyguard reached into a pocket and drew out a half-pint of the finest Irish whiskey. Artemis took the bottle and held it teasingly beyond the shadows. He barely had time to remove his goggles when the claw-like hand darted from the gloom to snatch the whiskey. A mottled green hand. There was no doubt.

Artemis swallowed a triumphant grin.

'Pay our friend, Butler. In full. Remember, Mister Nguyen, this is between us. You don't want Butler to come back, do you?'

'No, no, Master Fowl. My lips are sealed.'

'They had better be. Or Butler will seal them permanently.'

Nguyen skipped off down the alley, so relieved to be alive that he didn't even bother counting the sheaf of US currency. Most unlike him. In any event, it was all there. All twenty thousand dollars. Not bad for half an hour's work.

Artemis turned back to the healer.

'Now, madam, you have something that I want.'

The healer's tongue caught a drop of alcohol at the corner of her mouth.

'Yes, Irish. Sore head. Bad tooth. I heal.'

Artemis replaced the night-vision goggles and squatted to her level.

'I am perfectly healthy, madam, apart from a slight dust-mite allergy, and I don't think even you can do anything about that. No. What I want from you is your Book.'

The hag froze. Bright eyes glinted from beneath the shawl.

'Book?' she said cautiously. 'I don't know about no book. I am healer. You want book, go to library.'

Artemis sighed with exaggerated patience. 'You are no healer. You are a sprite, p'shóg, fairy, ka-dalun. Whichever language you prefer to use. And I want your Book.'

For a long moment the creature said nothing, then she threw back the shawl from her forehead. In the green glow of the night-vision goggles, her features leaped at Artemis like a Hallowe'en mask. The fairy's nose was long and hooked under two slitted golden eyes. Her ears were pointed, and the alcohol addiction had melted her skin like putty.

'If you know about the Book, human,' she said slowly, fighting the numbing effects of the whiskey, 'then you know about the magic I have in my fist. I can kill you with a snap of my fingers!'

Artemis shrugged. 'I think not. Look at you. You are near dead. The rice wine has dulled your senses. Reduced to healing warts. Pathetic. I am here to save you, in return for the Book.'

'What could a human want with our Book?'

'That is no concern of yours. All you need to know are your options.'

The sprite's pointed ears quivered. Options?

'One, you refuse to give us the Book and we go home, leaving you to rot in this sewer.'

'Yes,' said the fairy. 'I choose this option.'

'Ah no. Don't be so eager. If we leave without the Book, you will be dead in a day.'

'A day! A day!' The healer laughed. 'I will outlive you by a century. Even fairies tethered to the human realm can survive the ages.'

'Not with half a pint of holy water inside them,' said Artemis, tapping the now empty whiskey bottle.

The fairy blanched, then screamed, a high **keening** horrible sound.

'Holy water! You have murdered me, human.'

'True,' admitted Artemis. 'It should start to burn any minute now.'

The fairy poked her stomach tentatively. 'The second option?'

'Listening now, are we? Very well then. Option two. You give me the Book for thirty minutes only. Then I return your magic to you.'

The sprite's jaw dropped. 'Return my magic? Not possible.'

'Oh but it is. I have in my possession two **ampoules**. One, a vial of spring water from the fairy well sixty metres below the ring of Tara – possibly the most magical place on earth. This will counteract the holy water.'

'And the other?'

'The other is a little shot of man-made magic. A virus that feeds on alcohol, mixed with a growth **reagent**. It will flush every drop of rice wine from your body, remove the dependence and even bolster your failing liver. It'll be messy, but after a day you'll be zipping around as though you were a thousand years old again.'

The sprite licked her lips. To be able to rejoin the People? Tempting.

'How do I know to trust you, human? You have tricked me once already.'

'Good point. Here's the deal. I give you the water on faith. Then, after I've had a look at the Book, you get the booster. Take it or leave it.'

The fairy considered. The pain was already curling around her abdomen.

keening wailing or lamenting

ampoule small sealed glass container containing liquid

reagent substance or mixture used in chemical reactions

She thrust out her wrist.

'I take it.'

'I thought you might. Butler?'

The giant manservant unwrapped a soft Velcroed case containing a syringe gun and two vials. He loaded the clear one, shooting it into the sprite's clammy arm. The fairy stiffened momentarily, and then relaxed.

'Strong magic,' she breathed.

'Yes. But not as strong as your own will be when I give you the second injection. Now, the Book.'

The sprite reached into the folds of her filthy robe, rummaging for an age. Artemis held his breath. This was it. Soon the Fowls would be great again. A new empire would rise, with Artemis Fowl the Second at its head.

The fairy woman withdrew a closed fist.

'No use to you anyway. Written in the old tongue.'

Artemis nodded, not trusting himself to speak.

She opened her knobbly fingers. Lying in her palm was a tiny golden volume the size of a matchbox.

'Here, human. Thirty of your minutes. No more.'

Butler took the tiny tome reverentially. The bodyguard activated a compact digital camera and began photographing each wafer-thin page of the Book. The process took several minutes. When he was finished, the entire volume was stored on the camera's chip. Artemis preferred not to take chances with information. Airport security equipment had been known to wipe many a vital disk. So he instructed his aide to transfer the file to his portable phone and from there e-mail it to Fowl Manor in Dublin. Before the thirty minutes were up, the file containing every symbol in the Fairy Book was sitting safely in the Fowl server.

Artemis returned the tiny volume to its owner.

'Nice doing business with you.'

The sprite lurched to her knees. 'The other potion, human?'

Artemis smiled. 'Oh yes, the restoring booster. I suppose I did promise.'

'Yes. Human promised.'

'Very well. But before we administer it, I must warn you that purging is not pleasant. You're not going to enjoy this one bit.'

The fairy gestured around her at the squalid filth. 'You think I enjoy this? I want to fly again.'

Butler loaded the second vial, shooting this one straight into the **carotid artery**.

The sprite immediately collapsed on the mat, her entire frame quivering violently.

'Time to leave,' commented Artemis. 'A hundred years of alcohol leaving the body by any means possible is not a pretty sight.'

---

carotid artery artery carrying blood to the head and neck

② Creating the past

About the chapter

In this chapter, you will encounter a wide variety of historical fiction, from Rosemary Sutcliff's evocation of tenth-century Britain to Philip Pullman's description of a young woman's visit to a Victorian opium den. As you read, take the opportunity to think about why writers choose to set their stories in the past and why readers enjoy them so much.

About the text

Rosemary Sutcliff is the pioneer of historical fiction for younger readers. Many of her books have been televised and made into films.

The story is set in tenth-century Britain, a violent time when people lived in fear of Viking attack.

When he is twelve, Jestyn's mother dies and his stepfather tells him to leave home. Luckily, he is taken in by Gyrth, who employs him as a cattle-herd.

In this extract, there is a sudden storm and Jestyn is sent with his dog Brindle to get the yearlings (year-old cattle) away from the cliffs. On his way home he sees a Viking ship on the beach.

As you read, consider the following features of the text:

Word level

- Rosemary Sutcliff is careful to use vocabulary derived from Saxon words rather than Latin or French (*Ship-Chief* rather than *captain*). Can you find more examples?

Sentence level

- Look at the paragraph beginning, *The grip shifted ...* on page 29. How does Rosemary Sutcliff vary the sentence length and structure to create a feeling of excitement and tension?

Text level

- In real tenth-century Britain, most people in England spoke Saxon and the Vikings spoke Norse. How does the author use modern English but still make the story feel old?

- Jestyn is telling this story as an adult looking back. Look at how Rosemary Sutcliff makes him comment on the events from an adult perspective.

- What do you make of the *Forbidden Thing*? Notice how the writer incorporates the culture and beliefs of the past into her writing.

historical fiction

Blood Feud

by *Rosemary Sutcliff*

The Shore-Killing

I peered down through the wind and rain, and realized that it was a ship. Some ship that had come running for shelter before the storm, and either by luck or superb seamanship, was now beached safe in the lea of the rocks above the boiling tideline.

Merchantman or raider? It could be the same thing at times, for many a trading vessel of the Northmen **turned riever** on the way home from an unsuccessful voyage, or when they themselves had met with raiders and lost their cargo.

My heart began to race, and something within me shouted 'Danger!' as I pulled back from the cliff edge and turned in frantic haste to get the cattle away. But it was too late. We hadn't pushed on another spear throw, Brindle weaving to and fro at the heels of the jostling yearlings, when all at once the darkness among the wind-lashed **furze** bushes was alive with men.

Maybe there were no more than six or eight, but in the stormy darkness they might have been an army. The world burst into a reeling chaos of shouting men and bellowing cattle. The yearling were all ways at once. It did not last long. I pulled my knife from my belt and went for a big man who loomed suddenly before me. My foot slipped on the sodden turf, and naked steel went whitt-t-t past my ear as I pitched down. In all likelihood that fall saved my life. I had a moment's confused awareness of men and cattle above and all around me, and of Brindle springing with a snarl at the throat of one of the raiders; and then the flying hoof caught me on the side of the head, there was a burst of bright sparks inside my skull, and I went out into jagged darkness.

When I came back to myself, the rain had stopped, and I was sprawled on my back staring up at a blurred moon riding high in a sky of racing

turned riever became raiders

furze another term for gorse, a type of shrub

cloud-wrack. I lay for a while vaguely wondering where I was, and why my head hurt so much, until suddenly the memory of what had happened kicked me in the belly. I rolled on to my face and vomited, then got slowly on to one elbow and clawed myself up to my knees.

Under the booming of the wind and the surf, there was silence all about me. Nothing moved but the lashing furze branches: no men, no cattle. I managed to get up, the world dipping and swimming round me; and with my first step fell over something that brought me to my knees again. It was the body of old Brindle. I put out my hand and felt a sodden mass of hair with no life under it; and my hand came away sticky from the gaping hole in her throat. I wiped it on the grass. And as I did so, a kind of red wave rose from somewhere deep within me, engulfing all things save the thirst to kill.

In the years since then, I have come to know how large a part the blow on my head must have played in what followed after. Such a blow may make a man seem quite foolish, or see two of everything and wish only to sleep; or be for hours, maybe days, as though he were fighting drunk.

I felt about and found my knife, then got once more to my feet, and stumbled back to the place where I had first seen the fire in the cove. It was still there, and the ship-shadow beyond it, and a movement of figures, half seen in the flame-light. They would not care who saw their blaze, I thought, for when the Viking Kind come ashore, sensible folk stay away. It seemed to me that I was thinking quite clearly, and yet I did not think it at all foolish that I should be scrambling down the cliff path towards them, with a knife in my hand. They had killed my dog, the only thing I had to love, and I was going to kill as many of them as I could in return.

I slipped and half fell the last part of the way, picked myself up, knife still in hand, and charged on towards the dark figures round the fire. I was seeing everything through a red haze, but sharp-edged and for one instant frozen into stillness like a picture on a wall: the battered ship, the wind-torn fire, the carcasses of three yearlings lying on the blood-stained shingle while great joints hacked from them were already half-cooking, half-scorching on spear points over the heart of the blaze, the men in rough dark seamen's clothes, their faces all turned towards me as I ran.

historical fiction

Why they did not kill me then, I shall never know. A flung spear would have brought me down easily enough. Maybe, seeing that I was alone, it seemed scarce worth the trouble at least until they had had a bit of fun first.

Then I was among them, and the scene splintered out of its stillness. Someone stepped into my path, grinning. I saw the white animal flash of teeth in a wind-burned face, and the firelight on the blade of a **dirk**, and hurled myself forward, choking with the rage and grief that was in me. 'You killed my dog! Devils! You killed my dog!' There was a blare of laughter, and an arm came round me from behind, crushing me back against somebody's body. My dagger hand was caught and wrenched upward. I fought like a trapped animal, and when the knife was twisted from my grasp, ducked my head and bit into the arm that held me. I tasted blood between my teeth, and the laughter turned to a bellow of surprise and pain, but the grip never slackened.

'Ach! It bites like a wolf-cub!' somebody said. The Norse is kin to the Saxon tongue, and even through the red haze, I could understand after a fashion.

'It's the herdboy. Didn't you kill it, then?'

'Seems not. But that's a matter easy to set right.'

'You killed my dog!' I yelled again.

'It gives tongue like a wolf-cub too.'

The grip shifted, a giant of a man loomed up in front of me, and the point of a dagger was tickling my throat.

dirk short dagger

'So now we kill you too, and that will make all neat and ship-shape,' he said gravely. The rest crowded round, laughing. I had ceased to struggle, and stood still, knowing – but as though I were standing aside and knowing it of somebody else – that in a few more breaths I should be dead.

But another man, who seemed to be the chief, struck the dagger aside. 'Leave that.'

The giant turned on him, showing his teeth a little, but lowering his dagger-hand nonetheless. 'Why? Is he a long lost brother of yours?'

'Do not you be a fool, Aslak; what use is he to us dead? We can't eat him as we can the cattle–'

'There's not a good mouthful on his bones anyway,' someone guffawed, 'and wolf meat's too strong for my stomach.'

'And alive, he'll fetch his price in the Dublin Slave Market. We haven't done so well, this trip, that we can afford to toss aside a bit of easy profit that falls into our hands.'

There was a general growl of agreement; and the giant with the dagger shrugged, half laughing, and thrust the blade back into his belt.

'Tie him up and dump him against the rocks yonder, out of the way.' The man who seemed to be their chief jerked his thumb towards the sheltering outcrop.

So they bound my ankles together, and lashed my wrists behind me, with cords that somebody brought from the boat; and hauled me over to the rocks and flung me down there like a calf for branding; and went back to their own affairs.

Everything had begun to go far off and hazy; and I knew very little more, until suddenly – it must have been a good while later – the meat was cooked, and somebody was jabbing a sizzling lump of it against my mouth on the point of a dagger, shouting, 'Eat! If we do not kill you, eat!'

The chief nodded, grinning from ear to ear, with a lump of fat hanging half out of his mouth. 'It is you – your people that give the meat; now it is fair that you feast with the rest of us.'

And a third man struck in: 'A good host should always set his guests at their ease by eating with them himself.'

'And since no other one of your people seems coming to join the feast ...'

'I am thinking it's not often you fill your belly full of the good red

historical fiction

beef you herd for them.'

And that was true enough; and the lump of meat was still jabbing against my teeth. And I opened my mouth and ate.

Not because I was afraid they would kill me if I did not, but for a mingling of reasons that went deeper than that. I thought what did I owe to my mother's kind? And what did it matter? What did anything matter? Old Brindle was dead.

So I ate the meat, knew, even as I did so, that now I could never go back to the world that was only just behind me. Even if I were not, in all likelihood, going to be killed, even if I were not going to be sold in the Dublin slave market, I could not go back. I had broken the Tabu, the unwritten Law of Spirit, that binds all herdsman, eaten the stolen flesh of the cattle I herded; I had done the Forbidden Thing. I threw most of it up again soon after, but that was merely the blow on my head. I had done the Forbidden Thing, and there could be no going back.

I ate, and threw up, and slept. And when I woke, still with a splitting head, it was morning, and the seas had gentled, and the men were running their ship down into the surf.

They stowed the uneaten meat below the **thwarts**, and myself along with it. They had slackened off my ankle ropes and rebound my hands in front of me. (Every cattleman knows that the better the condition of his **steers** when they come to market, the better price they will fetch.)

So, they pushed out into the shallows; and lying among the cargo bales and the meat, I looked up past the swinging backs of the rowers, and saw against the drifting sky, and the cliff tops sinking astern, the dark figure of the Ship-Chief standing braced at the steering oar. I heard his rhythmic shout – 'Lift her! Lift her!' – and felt for the first time the liveness of a ship beneath me, lifting and twisting and dipping into the long swell of the Western seas.

The red haze of my rage had left me, and I felt cold and sick, and empty of all things. I could not even grieve for old Brindle any more. It all seemed so long ago.

thwart crosspiece of a ship forming the seat for a rower

steer another term for bullock

About the text

In this story, Jeremy Strong shows what fun can be had when you take liberties with the past. It may help if you know a little history (for example, who *really* built St Paul's Cathedral)!

As you read, consider the following features of the text:

Word level

- Look at the direct speech. How does Jeremy Strong make it sound '17th century'?

- The writer has some fun with the names – look at them closely.

Sentence level

- Consider how the writer has chosen to write in a very straightforward style suitable for younger readers.

- Look at the paragraph beginning, *Christopher's head …* on page 36. How does the writer introduce Christopher's thoughts?

Text level

- The story relies for its effectiveness on the reader having some historical knowledge.

- It also uses anachronism (for example, *the dishwasher*) to make us laugh.

- Is there a serious point being made about the importance of chance in the way events turn out?

London Rises from the Ashes
(and how it nearly all went wrong)

by Jeremy Strong

THE STREETS OF LONDON were still smouldering even though many days had passed since the Great Fire had given its final flicker. The ground, two foot deep in some places with ash and embers, was hot to walk on. Titus Drumm danced and jigged as he made his way along all that was left of Snout Lane, his gorgeous lace-frilled cuffs flopping about his hands like a host of attendant doves.

'Oh! Ouch!' The charcoal had burned through the soles of both boots, his *best* boots no less. Titus was not simply in pain; he was cross. He could not find the house he was looking for (because it had burnt to the ground along with everything else), and now he could not remember *who* he was looking for.

Titus danced up the road, sweating beneath his heavy wig, trying to recall what His Majesty King Charles II had told him. His Royal Highness was most anxious to rebuild the city. Most of London had gone up in flames, including the great church of St Paul. King Charles wanted it replaced, at once.

'The people must see that we are repairing the city. There is no time to be lost. I want every new building made from stone or brick – anything that won't catch fire. My tailor's shop was almost consumed by flames – a near disaster! Get Christopher Wren to draw up plans and start work immediately,' the King had boomed from on high (he was six foot two inches tall), before turning back to the large gilt mirror in order to admire his new silk hosiery and fabulously huge hat. 'Now I must be off to see that woman who has such nice oranges.'

'Yes Sire, at once Sire,' Titus had beamed as he reversed, bowing and scraping and tripping over his own lace boot tops. He had silently cursed the frothy garters. French they might be. Fashionable they might be. But they weren't much good if they were liable to break a man's neck.

Now Titus pranced up Snout Lane and tried to remember the name of England's great architect. 'Oh la-de-dah, I know it was a bird,' he muttered. 'Christopher Robin? Owl? Wagtail? Corncrake? What was it?'

All around him ragged figures poked amongst the ruins of buildings. A few carts, laden with rescued belongings, jerked and jolted past him, the horses pulling with bowed heads. The stench of burnt wood, burnt cloth, burnt fur and burnt skin filled the dark air. A dishevelled figure detached itself from the smoking skeleton of a house. The woman's face, arms and dress were all smeared with soot where she had been grovelling amongst the remains of her charred home.

'Good woman,' called Titus. 'Does not England's greatest architect live near here?'

'Oh my, it's Lord High-an'-Mighty 'imself. I don't know of no great arky-whatsit. Look.' The woman thrust a small bit of blackened wood into Titus's face. 'Know what that is?'

'Indeed I don't.'

'Knock on it,' she commanded. 'Go on. Knock on it.'

Titus felt a trifle embarrassed, but he

rapped the little piece of wood with his knuckles.

'Come in! That's my front door that is, what you's knockin' on. All that's left of it. Come in!'

'I'm sorry,' mumbled Titus.

'Don't matter,' said the woman matter-of-factly. 'Ain't no house for it to stick on anyways.'

Titus tried again. 'I'm looking for a man who designs things; goes by the name of a bird. Christopher something-or-other.'

'Ah,' mused the woman, 'that'll be Mister Thrush.'

'That's it!' cried Titus, at once forgetting his burning feet. 'Thrush! Does he live near by?'

'He would if he could.'

'What do you mean by that?'

'I mean that this was 'is house, an' a flea would be hard-pressed to live in it now, what with the state it's in, an' I can tell you we weren't short of fleas afore the fire. 'Ad enough fleas to stuff a pillow, so the lodger told me, an' he 'ad the bites to prove it an' all.' The grimy woman fixed Titus with one eye. 'I am Mistress Jellicoe sir, Mr Thrush's servant, what does 'is cookin' an' cleanin' an' chamberpot emptying' an' such. If you want the master you'll have to go to The Beggar's Armpit. It's about the only tavern still standin' around here.'

Titus fiddled in his purse and produced a silver sovereign. 'Thank you, thank you my good woman!' he cried, and he strode off toward the tavern.

Mistress Jellicoe watched him disappear, tested the coin on her black teeth and carried on muttering. 'I ain't a good woman, not good at all. I put a mouse in Mr Thrush's soup once … an' it couldn't swim.'

The Beggar's Armpit was in one of the few areas that had escaped the Great Fire, tucked down a dingy alleyway that stank of rotting food and emptied chamberpots. The old wooden houses were so ancient that they actually appeared to be propping each other up, like crumbling crones no longer able to stand on their own feet. Now the tavern itself was seething with refugees from the fire: noisy men and rowdy women and slopping ale.

Christopher Thrush – designer, inventor and possible genius – sat in the dingiest corner, cursing his luck. His house had burnt down before his eyes, along with his latest invention, the world's first dishwasher, almost completed. It would have made him rich and famous. Now he had nothing. He buried his pinched face in his leather tankard and sipped the dregs of beer, wishing that he was dead.

It was at this moment of deepest despair that a vision appeared before him, a vision that came in the portly, lace be-ribboned shape of Titus Drumm. The King's messenger bowed low, pulled forward a stool, parked his ample backside upon it and beamed at Christopher.

'Mr Thrush? I am here on a mission from His Majesty the King. He requires you to oversee the rebuilding of London, and he wishes you to commence work on the new church of St Paul at once.'

Christopher Thrush was so astonished that the first thing he did was punch Titus hard on the nose. The poor messenger tumbled backwards into a pool of spilled cider. At once Christopher was on his feet, helping the dazed man rise from the filthy rush floor and brushing down his ornate **doublet**. Christopher seized the messenger's wig from the puddle, squeezed half a pint of old cider from the wool ringlets and carefully arranged it back on Titus's shaven pate. Bits of rush poked out from beneath.

'I am so very sorry sir, but in my misery I thought you must be a dream that had come to taunt me. Now I see the blood pouring out of your nose I realise that you are indeed flesh and – well, blood indeed. Is this your tooth on the floor? My dear sir, this is wonderful news. The King really wants *me*?'

'Indeed,' grunted Titus, dabbing his nose with his perfumed hanky. 'You are to start work at once.'

Christopher's head almost spun with joy and invention. The buildings he would erect! The houses! The churches! His brain seethed with fabulous creations, and the most remarkable of all was the new church of St Paul. All night long he sketched his design. By the time morning came he had the plans for the most extraordinary church England would ever see.

Christopher hurried out into the early

doublet short, close-fitting padded jacket

historical fiction

morning air; still carrying the stink of charred wood, and hailed a passing **sedan chair**. 'Take me to Titus Drumm!' cried the genius, waving his master plan at the two ragged carriers. 'I am going to save London!'

One of the men glanced ruefully at the smouldering houses all around. 'What are you going to do?' he asked. 'Wee on it?'

But Christopher was already clambering into the sedan. A moment later he was hoisted into the air and the carriers were off at a gangly gallop. Inside, Christopher was bumped up and down and hurled about in general, but was far too excited to notice. His plan for St Paul's was a masterpiece.

Unfortunately Titus Drumm didn't agree. Titus studied the plan from every angle and at last he made an observation. 'La-de-dah,' he sighed. 'It's round, like a pig's bladder for playing football.'

'A ball, like the earth,' explained Christopher. 'The new church is like a model of God's earth itself.'

'But there are no windows,' Titus growled. 'How does any light pierce the gloom of this earth of yours?'

'Ah! That's one of my surprises – there *is* no roof! Light comes pouring straight in from above.'

'But so will the rain,' Titus pointed out. 'The congregation won't like getting wet.'

'Ah!' cried Christopher again. 'The rain won't fall on them. It will fall upon the Garden of Eden.'

'Really?' Titus was beginning to look round for help, for someone who would rescue him from this madman. In the depths of his mind a suspicion was beginning to stir. Christopher THRUSH?

'Yes,' Christopher went on eagerly. 'Inside the globe is a miniature Garden of Eden, raised upon marble pillars – a real garden, like a miniature forest, with plants and trees and all flowering things. There will be tigers roaming and elephants and … '

'Tigers and elephants roaming in the church! La-de-dah!' Titus clutched a chair for support.

'… and monkeys in the trees and great pythons and bats and birds of all kinds: parrots and humming birds, penguins, giant ostriches, the tiny wren … '

'WREN!' yelled Titus Drumm. Of course – Christopher *Wren*! Relief flooded through him. Hurrah! He pulled a purse full of sovereigns from his pocket and thrust it into Christopher's surprised hands. 'Here, take this money and your plan and go away. It won't do. The King doesn't want elephants and monkeys. Go, go!'

Even as he spoke, Titus was pushing Christopher out. A moment later the door slammed on the inventor and he was left standing bewildered on the street.

Christopher Thrush trudged wearily back towards The Beggar's Armpit, once again in despair. But the nearer he came to the tavern the more he brightened up. He had a full purse of silver in his pocket. He could begin work on that amazing new invention of his again. He would be famous and rich …

So it was that while Sir Christopher Wren got to work on the new St Paul's Cathedral, Christopher Thrush got back to work on the world's first dishwasher. It looked like a wardrobe sitting on the back of a cart, harnessed to two horses.

This was because it *was* a wardrobe sitting on the back of a cart, harnessed to two horses.

Christopher opened the wardrobe door to show puzzled onlookers the inside. 'My servant Mrs Jellicoe has placed all the dirty porcelain, all the filthy pots and pans inside here,' he explained, pointing at the packed shelves. 'On top is a tank of clean, hot water. I shut the door and pull this chain so … '

There was a gurgle and gush as the tank emptied into the wardrobe. A few drops leaked out through the door.

'The dishwasher is now ready.'

Christopher took the leading horse by the reins and walked it up the mud-rutted road. 'As the dishwasher passes over the bumps in this road the pots and pans are shaken about in the water until they are quite clean,' he shouted above the clattering noise from inside. 'This saves everyone a great labour. And now the washing is done. Behold!' He flung wide the wardrobe door.

To avoid embarrassing Christopher Thrush any further the recounting of this story concludes here.

historical fiction

About the text

Philip Pullman is one of the UK's most popular and well-respected authors for young readers. He usually writes either fantasy or historical fiction. *The Ruby in the Smoke* is set in Victorian London.

After her father is drowned in suspicious circumstances in the South China Sea, Sally Lockhart is left to fend for herself in London. Before long she is in terrible danger.

In this extract, she goes to visit an opium den with her photographer friend, Frederick.

As you read, consider the following features of the text:

Word level

- Philip Pullman uses a number of Victorian words and phrases (for example, *omnibus*).

- Look at how he writes Madame Chang's speech. What effect does this have?

Sentence level

- Notice how Philip Pullman includes description in his writing. Look closely at the paragraph beginning, *They set off …* on page 42. We learn about the inhabitants of Limehouse, Sally's reactions and Frederick's character – all in one paragraph.

- How does Pullman use sentence structure to portray Sally's dream?

Text level

- The writer has set himself some challenging tasks in this episode. The Victorian attitude to ethnic minorities was very different from our own. How can he write about the Chinese owner of an opium den without coming across as racist?

- How can he enable readers with little historical knowledge to appreciate the politics of the opium trade?

The Ruby in the Smoke

by Philip Pullman

MADAME CHANG

Next afternoon, Frederick took Sally to the East End.

The year before, he had helped his uncle in a project to photograph scenes of London life, using an experimental magnesium light. The light had only been partly successful, but Frederick had made a number of acquaintances in the course of the project, including the proprietress of a Limehouse opium den: a lady by the name of Madame Chang.

'Most of these places are abominable,' he said as they sat in the omnibus. 'A shelf to lie on, a filthy blanket, and a pipe and that's all. But Madame Chang takes care of her customers, and keeps the place clean. I suppose the reason is that she doesn't take the stuff herself.'

'Are they always Chinese? Why doesn't the government stop them?'

'Because the government grows the stuff itself, and sells it, and makes a handsome profit.'

'Surely not!'

'Don't you know anything of history?'

'Well – no.'

'We fought a war thirty years ago over opium. The Chinese objected to

English merchants smuggling opium into the country, and tried to ban it; so we went to war and forced them to take it. They grow it in India, you see, under government supervision.'

'But that's horrible! And our government's still doing that now? I don't believe it.'

'You'd better ask Madame Chang. Time to get out now; we'll walk the rest of the way.'

The omnibus had stopped at the West India Dock Station. Beyond the gate into the dock, a line of warehouses stretched for over half a mile to the left, and above their roofs the masts of ships and the jibs of cranes pointed to the grey sky like skeletal fingers.

They set off to the right, towards the river. They passed the large square Dock Offices, where she supposed her father must have come many times on business, and then turned down an alley and into a maze of courts and sidestreets. Some of them were not even named, but Frederick knew the way, and never hesitated. Barefoot children, ragged and filthy, played among the rubbish and the streams of stinking water that trickled thickly over the cobbles. Women standing in their doorways fell silent as they passed, and stared with hostile eyes, arms folded, until they had gone by. They look so old, thought Sally; even the children had pinched, old-men's faces, with wrinkled brows and tight-drawn lips. Once they came on a group of men at the entrance to a narrow court. Some were leaning on the wall, some squatting on doorsteps. Their clothes were torn

historical fiction

and clotted with dirt, their eyes were full of hatred, and one of them stood up and two others shifted away from the wall as Frederick and Sally approached, as if to challenge their right to pass. But Frederick did not change pace. He walked straight up to the entrance, and the men drew aside at the last moment, looking away.

'Unemployed, poor fellows,' said Frederick when they'd turned the corner, 'It's either the street corner or the workhouse, and who'd choose the workhouse?'

'But there must be jobs on the ships, or at the docks, or something. People always want workers, don't they?'

'No, they don't. You know, Sally, there are things in London that make opium look no more harmful than tea.'

She supposed he meant poverty, and as she looked around she had to agree.

Presently they came to a low wooden door set in the wall of a grimy alley. There was a sign beside the doorway, with some Chinese characters painted in black on red. Frederick tugged the bell-handle, and after a minute the door was opened by an old Chinaman. He was dressed in a loose black silk robe, and he had a skull-cap and a pigtail. He bowed to them and stood aside as they entered.

Sally looked around. They were in a hall lined with delicately painted wallpaper; all the wood was lacquered in a deep, lustrous red, and an ornate lantern hung from the ceiling. There was a close, sweet smell in the air.

The servant left, to come back after a moment with a middle-aged Chinese woman in a richly embroidered robe. Her hair was severely pinned back, and she had black silk trousers under the robe, and red slippers on her tiny feet. She bowed, and gestured towards an inner room.

'Please consent to enter my poor place of business,' she said. Her voice was low and musical, and quite without any accent. 'You, sir, are Mr Frederick Garland, the photographic artist. But I have not been honoured with the acquaintance of your beautiful companion.'

They entered the room. While Frederick explained who Sally was and what they wanted, Sally looked around in wonder. The light was very dim; only two or three Chinese lanterns penetrated the smoky darkness. Everything that could be painted or lacquered in the room was the same deep blood-red, and the door-posts and the beams of the ceiling were carved with curling, snarling dragons picked out in gold. It gave her a sense of oppressive richness; it seemed as if the room had taken on the shape of the collective dreams of all those who had ever gone there to seek oblivion. At intervals around the walls – it was a large, long room – were low couches, and on each of them was lying a man, apparently asleep. But no! There was a woman, hardly older than Sally herself; and here another, in middle age; respectably dressed, too. And then one of the sleepers stirred, and the old servant hastened up with a long pipe, and knelt on the floor to prepare it.

Frederick and Madame Chang were speaking in low voices behind her. Sally looked for somewhere to sit; she felt dizzy. The smoke from the newly lit pipe drifted up to her, sweet and enticing and curious. She breathed in once, and then again, and –

Darkness suddenly. Stifling heat.

She was in the Nightmare.

She lay still, with her eyes wide open, searching the darkness. An enormous **convulsive** fear was squeezing her heart. She tried to move, but could not – and yet it didn't feel as if she were bound; her limbs were too weak to move.

And she knew that only a moment earlier, she'd been awake …

But she was so afraid. The fear grew and grew. It was worse than ever this time, because it was so much clearer. She knew that any second, close to her in the darkness, a man would begin to scream, and she began to cry in pure fear of it. And then it started.

The scream ripped through the darkness like a sharp sword. She thought she would die from fear. But voices were speaking! This was new – and they were not speaking in English – and yet she could understand them –

'Where is it?'

'Not with me! I pray – I beg of you – it is with a friend –'

'They are coming! Be quick!'

And then a hideous sound, the sound of a sharp instrument sinking into meat – a sort of tearing sound, followed by a sudden gasp and groan as if all the breath had been forced out of a man's lungs at once: and then a gushing, splashing sound that quickly died away into a trickle.

Light.

There was a tiny spark of light somewhere.

(Oh, but she was awake, in the opium den! This was impossible –)

convulsive involuntary and violent

historical fiction

And she could not escape from the dream. It unwound ceaselessly, and she had to live through it. She knew what was coming next: a guttering candle, a man's voice –

'Look! Look at him! My God –'

It was the voice of Major Marchbanks!

This was the point where she had always woken up before – but now something else happened. The light came closer and was held out to one side, and the face of a young man looked down at her: fierce, darkly moustached, with glittering eyes and a trickle of blood down his cheek.

All at once she was awash with fear. She was almost mad with it. She thought, I'm going to die – no one can be afraid like this and not die or go mad …

There was a sharp blow on her cheek. She heard the sound of it a second later; things were out of joint, and everything was dark again. She felt a desolating sense of loss –

And then she was awake, on her knees, her face streaming with tears. Frederick was kneeling beside her, and without thinking she flung her arms around his neck and sobbed. He held her tightly and said nothing. They were in the hall: When had she moved out there? Madame Chang stood a little way off, watching closely.

When she saw that Sally was conscious again, the Chinese woman stepped forward and bowed.

'Please to sit on the divan, Miss Lockhart. Li Chang will bring some refreshment.'

She clapped her hands. Frederick helped her on to the silk-covered divan, and the old servant offered her a little porcelain cup containing some hot fragrant drink. She sipped it and felt her head clearing.

'What happened? How long was I –'

'You were affected by the smoke,' said Frederick. 'You must have inhaled more than you thought. But to go under all at once like that – isn't that very unusual, Madame Chang?'

'This was not her first encounter with the smoke,' said the lady, still standing motionlessly in the gloom.

'I've never smoked opium in my life!' said Sally.

'It distresses me to contradict you, Miss Lockhart. But you have breathed the smoke before. I have seen ten thousand who have taken the smoke, and I know. What did you see in your vision?'

'A scene that – that's come to me many times. A nightmare. A man is being killed and … And two other men come along and … What can it be, Madame Chang? Am I going mad?'

She shook her head.

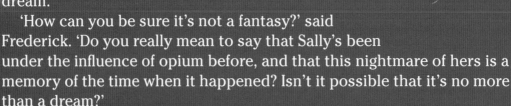

'The power of the smoke is unbounded. It hides secrets of the past so well that the sharpest eyes in the brightest daylight would never find them; and then it reveals them all like buried treasure when they have been forgotten. What you saw is a memory, Miss Lockhart, not a dream.'

'How can you be sure it's not a fantasy?' said Frederick. 'Do you really mean to say that Sally's been under the influence of opium before, and that this nightmare of hers is a memory of the time when it happened? Isn't it possible that it's no more than a dream?'

'It is possible, Mr Garland. But it is not what happened. I can see plainly what is invisible to you, just as a doctor can see plainly what is troubling his patient. There are a hundred and one signs by which these things may be read, but if you cannot read them, you will see nothing.'

Her still figure spoke out of the gloom like the priestess of some ancient cult, full of authority and wisdom. Sally felt the urge to weep again.

She stood up.

'Thank you for explaining, Madame Chang,' she said. 'Am I … Am I in danger from the drug? Now that I've taken it once, will I crave to take it again?'

'You have taken it twice, Miss Lockhart,' said the lady. 'If you are in danger, it is not from the drug. But you have the smoke in your nature now. It has revealed something you did not know; maybe you will crave the smoke not for its own sake, but for the sake of what it can show you.'

She bowed, and Frederick stood up to leave. Sally, who still felt dizzy, took the arm he offered, and after exchanging farewells, they left.

Outside, it was nearly dark. The cold air was welcome to Sally, who breathed it in gratefully, and soon found the pounding in her head diminish a little. Before long, they were in the Commercial Road, and the bustle of traffic, the gaslights, the glowing shop-windows made the opium den seem like a dream itself. But she still trembled, and her sides and back were wet with perspiration.

historical fiction

3

Exploring the unknown

About the chapter

Science fiction developed relatively recently (about two hundred years ago) but it rapidly became one of the most important and popular genres of fiction. This chapter contains an extract from *Frankenstein*, generally considered to be the first sci-fi story (although it is often referred to as a 'Horror' story) and extracts from a wide range of modern writers.

Before you start reading, think about all the examples of the genre that you have come across in books, films and television. What do they all have in common?

science fiction

About the text

Since we first looked up into the sky, humans have wondered if there is life on other planets. Science-fiction writers, however, took that thought one stage further and asked what would happen if aliens looked at Earth, and then decided that they wanted to invade it. Published in 1898, H.G. Wells' novel *The War of the Worlds* imagines Earth invaded by powerful Martians. In this extract, he describes what happens after the spaceships land in Kent.

As you read, consider the following features of the text:

Word level

- H.G. Wells contrasts the words of his narrator with the words spoken by members of the crowd (for example, *A lank tentacular appendage* and *I'm a-goin' 'ome, I am*). What effect does this have?

- How can you tell that this novel was written at the end of the nineteenth century rather than more recently?

Sentence level

- How do the writer's sentence structure and use of punctuation create tension and suspense? Look at the varying sentence lengths and the use of dashes in the paragraph beginning, *A sudden chill … .*

- H.G. Wells is attempting to give a second-by-second account of what took place. Some sentences are very specific, almost scientific, while others are more impressionistic. Can you find examples of both?

- Look at the paragraph beginning, *I think everyone expected …* on page 50. Notice how H.G. Wells reveals the Martian.

Text level

- How does the writer express the thoughts and feelings of his narrator? Look at how he conveys his narrator's conflicting feelings of fascination and dread.

- Note how H.G. Wells keeps repeating the names of familiar places (for example, *Woking*). What effect would this have had on readers at the time?

- In the second part of the extract, the narrator observes events from a distance. What effect does this have?

The War of the Worlds
by H. G. Wells

The Cylinder Opens

When I returned to the common the sun was setting. Scattered groups were hurrying from the direction of Woking, and one or two persons were returning. The crowd about the pit had increased, and stood out black against the lemon yellow of the sky – a couple of hundred people, perhaps. There were raised voices, and some sort of struggle appeared to be going on about the pit. Strange imaginings passed through my mind. As I drew nearer I heard Stent's voice:

"Keep back! Keep back!"

A boy came running towards me.

"It's a-movin'," he said to me as he passed; "a-screwin' and a-screwin' out. I don't like it. I'm a-goin' 'ome, I am."

I went on to the crowd. There were really, I should think, two or three hundred people elbowing and jostling one another, the one or two ladies there being by no means the least active.

"He's fallen in the pit!" cried some one.

"Keep back!" said several.

The crowd swayed a little, and I elbowed my way through. Every one seemed greatly excited. I heard a peculiar humming sound from the pit.

"I say!" said Ogilvy; "help keep these idiots back. We don't know what's in the **confounded** thing, you know!"

I saw a young man, a shop assistant in Woking I believe he was, standing on the cylinder and trying to scramble out of the

---

confounded damned

hole again. The crowd had pushed him in.

The end of the cylinder was being screwed out from within. Nearly two feet of shining screw projected. Somebody blundered against me, and I narrowly missed being pitched onto the top of the screw. I turned, and as I did so the screw must have come out, for the lid of the cylinder fell upon the gravel with a ringing **concussion**. I stuck my elbow into the person behind me, and turned my head towards the Thing again. For a moment that circular cavity seemed perfectly black. I had the sunset in my eyes.

I think everyone expected to see a man emerge – possibly something a little unlike us terrestrial men, but in all essentials a man. I know I did. But, looking, I presently saw something stirring within the shadow: greyish **billowy** movements, one above another, and then two luminous disks – like eyes. Then something resembling a little grey snake, about the thickness of a walking stick, coiled up out of the writhing middle, and wriggled in the air towards me – and then another.

A sudden chill came over me. There was a loud shriek from a woman behind. I half turned, keeping my eyes fixed upon the cylinder still, from which other tentacles were now projecting, and

began pushing my way back from the edge of the pit. I saw astonishment giving place to horror on the faces of the people about me. I heard inarticulate exclamations on all sides. There was a general movement backwards. I saw the shopman struggling still on the edge of the pit. I found myself alone, and saw the people on the other side of the pit running off, Stent among them. I looked again at the cylinder, and ungovernable terror gripped me. I stood petrified and staring.

A big greyish rounded bulk, the size, perhaps, of a bear, was rising slowly and painfully out of the cylinder. As it bulged up and caught the light, it glistened like wet leather.

Two large dark-coloured eyes were regarding me steadfastly. The mass that framed them, the head of the thing, was rounded, and had, one might say, a face. There was a mouth under the eyes, the lipless brim of which quivered and panted, and dropped saliva. The whole creature heaved and pulsated convulsively. A lank tentacular **appendage** gripped the edge of the cylinder, another swayed in the air.

Those who have never seen a living Martian can scarcely imagine the strange horror of its appearance. The peculiar V-shaped mouth with its pointed upper lip, the absence of brow ridges, the absence of a chin beneath the wedgelike lower lip, the incessant quivering of this

concussion violent shaking, shock

billowy soft upward-curving

appendage something that is attached

mouth, the Gorgon groups of tentacles, the tumultuous breathing of the lungs in a strange atmosphere, the evident heaviness and painfulness of movement due to the greater gravitational energy of the earth – above all, the extraordinary intensity of the immense eyes – were at once vital, intense, inhuman, crippled and monstrous. There was something **fungoid** in the oily brown skin, something in the clumsy deliberation of the tedious movements unspeakably nasty. Even at this first encounter, this first glimpse, I was overcome with disgust and dread.

Suddenly the monster vanished. It had toppled over the brim of the cylinder and fallen into the pit, with a thud like the fall of a great mass of leather. I heard it give a peculiar thick cry, and forthwith another of these creatures appeared darkly in the deep shadow of the **aperture**.

I turned and, running madly, made for the first group of trees, perhaps a hundred yards away; but I ran slantingly and stumbling, for I could not avert my face from these things.

There, among some young pine trees and furze bushes, I stopped, panting, and waited further developments. The common round the sand pits was dotted with people, standing like myself in a half-fascinated terror, staring at these creatures, or rather at the heaped gravel at the edge of the pit in which

fungoid resembling fungus

aperture gap, opening

they lay. And then, with a renewed horror, I saw a round, black object bobbing up and down on the edge of the pit. It was the head of the shopman who had fallen in, but showing as a little black object against the hot western sun. Now he got his shoulder and knee up, and again he seemed to slip back until only his head was visible. Suddenly he vanished, and I could have fancied a faint shriek had reached me. I had a momentary impulse to go back and help him that my fears overruled.

Everything was then quite invisible, hidden by the deep pit and the heap of sand that the fall of the cylinder had made. Anyone coming along the road from Chobham or Woking would have been amazed at the sight – a dwindling multitude of perhaps a hundred people or more standing in a great irregular circle, in ditches, behind bushes, behind gates and hedges, saying little to one another and that in short, excited shouts, and staring, staring hard at a few heaps of sand. The barrow of ginger beer stood, a queer derelict, black against the burning sky, and in the sand pits was a row of deserted vehicles with their horses feeding out of nosebags or pawing the ground.

The Heat-Ray

After the glimpse I had had of the Martians emerging from the cylinder in which they had come to the earth from their planet, a kind of fascination paralysed my actions. I remained standing knee-deep in the heather, staring at the mound that hid them. I was a battleground of fear and curiosity.

I did not dare to go back towards the pit, but I felt a passionate longing to peer into it. I began walking, therefore, in a big curve, seeking some point of vantage and continually looking at the sand heaps that hid these new-comers to our earth. Once a leash of thin black whips, like the arms of an octopus, flashed across the sunset and was immediately withdrawn, and afterwards a thin rod rose up, joint by joint, bearing at its apex a circular disk that spun with a wobbling motion. What could be going on there?

Most of the spectators had gathered in one or two groups – one a little crowd towards Woking, the other a knot of people in the direction of Chobham. Evidently they shared my mental conflict. There were few near me. One man I approached – he was, I perceived, a neighbour of mine, though I did not know his name – and accosted. But it was scarcely a time for articulate conversation.

"What ugly brutes!" he said. "Good God! What ugly brutes!" He repeated this over and over again.

"Did you see a man in the pit?" I said; but he made no answer to that. We became silent, and stood watching for a time side by side, deriving, I fancy, a certain comfort in one another's company. Then I shifted my position to a little knoll that gave me the advantage of a yard or more of elevation and when I looked for him presently he was walking towards Woking.

The sunset faded to twilight before anything further happened. The crowd far away on the left, towards Woking, seemed to grow, and I heard now a faint murmur from it. The little knot of people towards Chobham dispersed. There was scarcely an **intimation** of movement from the pit.

It was this, as much as anything, that gave people courage, and I suppose the new arrivals from Woking also helped to restore confidence. At any rate, as the dusk came on a slow, intermittent movement upon the sand pits began, a movement that seemed to gather force as the stillness of the evening about the cylinder remained unbroken. Vertical black figures in twos and threes would advance, stop, watch, and advance again, spreading out as they did so in a thin

intimation	hint

science fiction

irregular crescent that promised to enclose the pit in its **attenuated** horns. I, too, on my side began to move towards the pit.

Then I saw some cabmen and others had walked boldly into the sand pits, and heard the clatter of hoofs and the grind of wheels. I saw a lad trundling off the barrow of apples. And then, within thirty yards of the pit, advancing from the direction of Horsell, I noted a little black knot of men, the foremost of whom was waving a white flag.

This was the **Deputation**. There had been a hasty consultation, and since the Martians were evidently, in spite of their repulsive forms, intelligent creatures, it had been resolved to show them, by approaching them with signals, that we too were intelligent.

Flutter, flutter, went the flag, first to the right, then to the left. It was too far for me to recognise anyone there, but afterwards I learned that Ogilvy, Stent, and Henderson were with others in this attempt at communication. This little group had in its advance dragged inward, so to speak, the circumference of the now almost complete circle of people, and a number of dim black figures followed it at discreet distances.

Suddenly there was a flash of light, and a quantity of luminous greenish smoke came out of the pit in three distinct puffs, which drove up, one after the other, straight into the still air.

This smoke (or flame, perhaps, would be the better word for it) was so bright that the deep blue sky overhead and the hazy stretches of brown common towards Chertsey, set with black pine trees, seemed to darken abruptly as these puffs arose, and to remain the darker after their dispersal. At the same time a faint hissing sound became audible.

Beyond the pit stood the little wedge of people with the white flag at its apex, arrested by these phenomena, a little knot of small vertical black shapes upon the black ground. As the green smoke arose, their faces flashed out pallid green, and faded again as it vanished. Then slowly the hissing passed into a humming, into a long, loud, droning noise. Slowly a humped shape rose out of the pit, and the ghost of a beam of light seemed to flicker out from it.

Forthwith flashes of actual flame, a bright glare leaping from one to another, sprang from the scattered group of men. It was as if some invisible jet **impinged** upon them and flashed into white flame. It was as if each man were suddenly and momentarily turned to fire.

Then, by the light of their own destruction, I saw them staggering and falling, and their supporters turning to run.

I stood staring, not as yet realising that this was death leaping from man to man in that little distant crowd. All I felt was that it was something very strange. An almost noiseless and blinding flash of light, and a man fell headlong and lay still; and as the unseen shaft of heat passed over them, pine trees burst into fire, and every dry furze bush became with one dull thud a mass of flames. And far away towards Knaphill I saw the flashes of trees and hedges and wooden buildings suddenly set alight.

---

attenuated thin, slender, tapered

deputation a group of people appointed to represent others

impinged made an impact

About the text

This is the opening of Lesley Howarth's novel *MapHead* in which she presents a very different view of an alien invasion. Unlike *The War of the Worlds*, this story is told from the point of view of the visitors, specifically MapHead himself, who comes from the Subtle World that exists side by side with our own.

As you read, consider the following features of the text:

Word level

- Lesley Howarth uses a number of contractions (for example, *It'd*). What effect does this have?

- Alongside the chatty style, she includes some scientific language.

Sentence level

- Look at the first sentence. Did you find it hard to understand at first? If so, why?

- Most of the sentences are short and simple. What effect does this have?

Text level

- In writing from the point of view of the aliens, Lesley Howarth has set herself a real challenge. The opening must be clear enough to make sense to you, as a reader, but mysterious and intriguing enough to make you want to read on. See if you can work out how the author has achieved this.

- Look at the way the author introduces a more personal theme towards the end of the extract. Can you predict how this will develop?

MapHead

by Lesley Howarth

Catshake

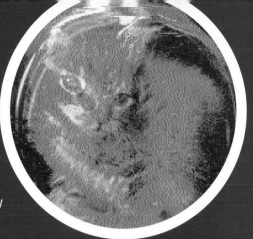

The reason Powers'd liquefied the cat in the end greenhouse first is it asked for it. It was a scrawny grey number with pleading yellow eyes and sticking-out hip bones, like it'd swallowed a box or something. It came mewling around at the slightest sniff of food. It'd even beg for tomatoes when it knew it couldn't eat them.

One evening, after a film, Powers turned his eyes on the scrawny grey cat. It was bad news for the cat. Under the power of Powers' eyes it quailed and fell down. It must've heaved in its skin a full ten seconds before its organs reduced. Then there was draining and disposal. And about two pints of catshake. "Enjoy," said Powers. Boothe grinned. He'd only been Boothe ten minutes. Really his name was MapHead. But already he felt the new name bite.

The end greenhouse was home, for the while. It was the largest of five great glasshouses on the tomato farm – and the furthest from the bungalow. Evenings, they usually wandered up the track and sat in their hollow place in the hedge. It was the ideal angle to catch the telly in the bungalow living-room. They always felt like munchies when they got back. It was just the cat's bad luck.

The film that night was The Emerald Forest. They both watched closely – but they saw no emeralds. They didn't really get it, at all. They'd been watching the film anyway when they spotted the name Powers Boothe in the credits and liked it so much they split it between them, Powers for father, Boothe for son. "When in Rome," said Powers.

"Sorry?" said Boothe.

"A saying," explained Powers, back in the greenhouse. "When in Rome, do as the Romans do. Now we're here, we'll have a proper name each."

"Romans?" said Boothe. Boothe was big on Romans. "Can we play Circus Maximus?"

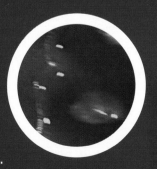

"No. No more Circus Maximus today."

Boothe sighed. It was only a game. But still. He drained his catshake, eyeing Powers over the top of his can. Powers wouldn't change his mind. He didn't know how.

"Hey," said Boothe. "Hey. What's protein status, catshake?"

"Where's your speech rhythms?" asked Powers sternly. "You should make it flow. Make it more natural."

Boothe paused. "Hey, Dad, what's in a cat?"

"Better," nodded Powers. "Much better."

Powers considered the catshake. He made some quick calculations. "I'd give it around fifty-eight per cent usable protein. Quite a bit of rubbish in a cat."

Only fifty-eight per cent. Boothe whistled. He liked the effect. He whistled some more. "Hey," he said again. "Hey."

Then he got up. He wandered down the tomato rows until he found a real killer. Post-box red and big as a fist, it plumped in his hand like a gift. He held it up, for a joke.

"Look. The tomato that ate the world." Powers looked blank. "How could it?" Powers took everything literally.

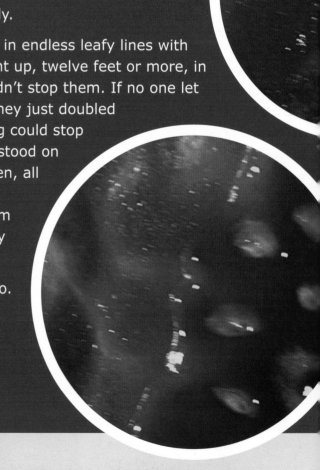

The tomato plants filled the greenhouse in endless leafy lines with walkways in between. They grew straight up, twelve feet or more, in the wheezing glass roof. But the roof didn't stop them. If no one let down their strings to give them room, they just doubled right over and grew downwards. Nothing could stop them. Even if the stem cracked, or you stood on them, they grew. They grew like madmen, all season. In between them zig-zagged enormous powdery bees. They went from flower to flower transferring pollen. They were unstoppable too.

Boothe sank his teeth in his killer tomato. It bombed his mouth with juice, but he didn't mind at all. Powers watched him eating. He didn't bother with tomatoes himself any more. Instead he drank the special growth fluid that fed the plants, sucking it straight from the tubes connecting every rootball to a meaty feeder pipe along the centre of every row. More logical, said Powers. All tomatoes did was change it into sugars.

Powers'd eat anything. He'd even tried a bee or two.

Boothe wiped his chin. He'd been Boothe fifteen minutes. He wasn't sure he liked it, now.

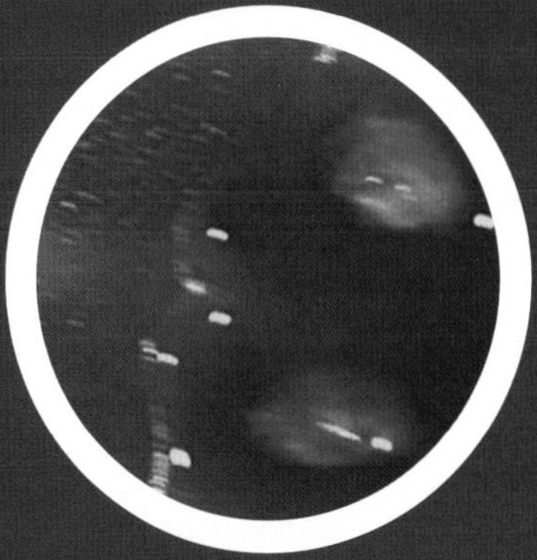

"Can I not be Boothe?"

"You are Boothe."

"I mean, can I not be?"

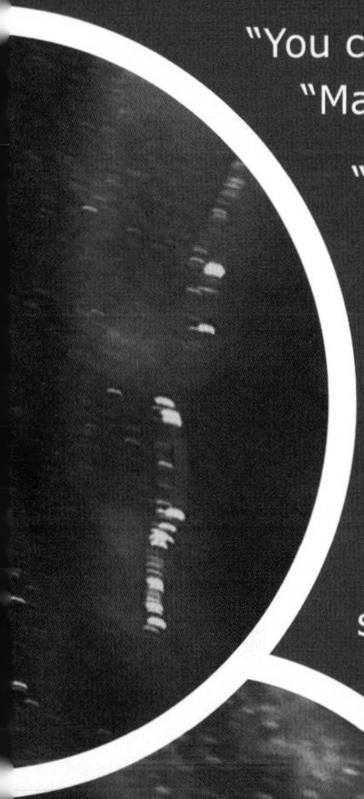

"You can't be MapHead," said Powers sharply. "MapHead isn't a name."

"I don't want to. Be Boothe."

"Speech rhythms. Why not?"

"I don't prefer."

"But Boothe's natural. It's a name."

Already MapHead was blushing a map of his home terrain over his domed head, the contour figures slipping and sliding over his skin, down his neck, the way he did when he was stressed.

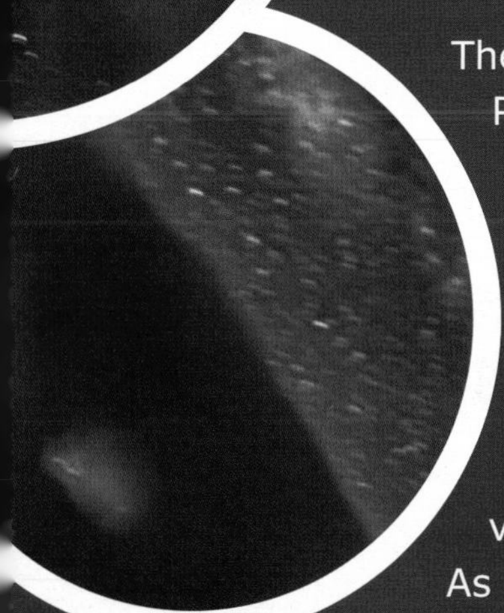

The fact was, he wasn't going to get natural overnight. Powers was natural. He fitted in pretty well. But Powers had visited this neck of the woods before, once or twice. Once, at any rate, some twelve years ago – else he, MapHead, wouldn't even be here, would he? Not unless his father had visited his mother in the beginning. No visit, no MapHead. Simple really.

Now they'd come back. That was simple too. No return visit, no known mother. She was the reason they'd come. As far back as MapHead could remember, she'd never been around. Powers had a story about how he'd met her. Sometimes he'd tell it, sometimes he wouldn't. Whenever he would, MapHead liked to hear it.

About the text

This unusual story asks us to see the human race from an alien perspective. It's not a pretty sight!

As you read, consider the following features of the text:

Word level

- Notice how the author mixes some 'sci-fi' technical language with what sounds like an everyday conversation. What effect does this have?

- Terry Bisson constantly repeats the word 'meat' to shock the reader. What sort of connotations does the word usually have?

Sentence level

- The writer constructs sentences to convey the attitude of each character. Can you find any differences between them?

- Why are some words and phrases underlined?

Text level

- Unusually, this story contains no prose narrative or description at all. In fact, it is closer to a playscript in its format. Why do you think Terry Bisson decided to write this way?

- Notice how the story is built around one character trying to convince the other.

- The story uses humour to make a serious point. What message do you think Bisson is trying to convey?

"They're made out of meat."
  "Meat?"
  "Meat. They're made out of meat."
  "Meat?"
  "There's no doubt about it. We picked up several from different parts of the planet, took them aboard our **recon** vessels, and probed them all the way through. They're completely meat."
  "That's impossible. What about the radio signals? The messages to the stars?"
  "They use the radio waves to talk, but the signals don't come from them. The signals come from machines."
  "So who made the machines? That's who we want to contact."
  "<u>They</u> made the machines. That's what I'm trying to tell you. Meat made the machines."
  "That's ridiculous. How can meat make a machine? You're

THEY'RE MADE OUT OF MEAT

by Terry Bisson

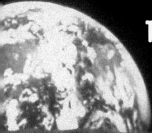

asking me to believe in **sentient** meat."

"I'm not asking you, I'm telling you. These creatures are the only sentient race in that sector and they're made out of meat."

"Maybe they're like the orfolei. You know, a carbon-based intelligence that goes through a meat stage."

"Nope. They're born meat and they die meat. We studied them for several of their life spans, which didn't take long. Do you have any idea what's the life span of meat?"

"Spare me. Okay, maybe they're only part meat. You know, like the weddilei. A meat head with an electron plasma brain inside."

"Nope. We thought of that, since they do have meat heads, like the weddilei. But I told you, we probed them. They're meat all the way through."

"No brain?"

"Oh, there's a brain all right. It's just that the brain is <u>made out of meat</u>! That's what I've been trying to tell you."

"So ... what does the thinking?"

"You're not understanding, are you? You're refusing to deal with what I'm telling you. The brain does the thinking. The meat."

"Thinking meat! You're asking me to believe in thinking meat!"

"Yes, thinking meat! Conscious meat! Loving meat. Dreaming meat. The meat is the whole deal! Are you beginning to get the picture or do I have to start all over?"

"Omigod. You're serious then. They're made out of meat."

"Thank you. Finally. Yes. They are indeed made out of meat. And they've been trying to get in touch

recon reconnaissance

sentient having the power of perception by the senses

with us for almost a hundred of their years."

"Omigod. So what does this meat have in mind?"

"First it wants to talk to us. Then I imagine it wants to explore the Universe, contact other sentiences, swap ideas and information. The usual."

"We're supposed to talk to meat."

"That's the idea. That's the message they're sending out by radio. 'Hello. Anyone out there. Anybody home.' That sort of thing."

"They actually do talk, then. They use words, ideas, concepts?"

"Oh, yes. Except they do it with meat."

"I thought you just told me they used radio."

"They do, but what do you think is on the radio? Meat sounds. You know how when you slap or flap meat, it makes a noise? They talk by flapping their meat at each other. They can even sing by squirting air through their meat."

"Omigod. Singing meat. This is altogether too much. So what do you advise?"

"Officially or unofficially?"

"Both."

"Officially, we are required to contact, welcome and log in any and all sentient races or multibeings in this **quadrant** of the Universe, without prejudice, fear or favor. Unofficially, I advise that we erase the records and forget the whole thing."

"I was hoping you would say that."

"It seems harsh, but there is a limit. Do we really want to make

---

quadrant each of four parts of a plane, sphere, space or body divided by two lines or planes at right angles

science fiction

contact with meat?"

"I agree one hundred percent. What's there to say? 'Hello, meat. How's it going?' But will this work? How many planets are we dealing with here?"

"Just one. They can travel to other planets in special meat containers, but they can't live on them. And being meat, they can only travel through C space. Which limits them to the speed of light and makes the possibility of their ever making contact pretty slim. **Infinitesimal**, in fact."

"So we just pretend there's no one home in the Universe."

"That's it."

"Cruel. But you said it yourself, who wants to meet meat? And the ones who have been aboard our vessels, the ones you probed? You're sure they won't remember?"

"They'll be considered crackpots if they do. We went into their heads and smoothed out their meat so that we're just a dream to them."

"A dream to meat! How strangely appropriate, that we should be meat's dream."

"And we marked the entire sector <u>unoccupied</u>."

"Good. Agreed, officially and unofficially. Case closed. Any others? Anyone interesting on that side of the galaxy?"

"Yes, a rather shy but sweet hydrogen core cluster intelligence in a class nine star in G445 zone. Was in contact two galactic rotations ago, wants to be friendly again."

"They always come around."

"And why not? Imagine how unbearably, how unutterably cold the Universe would be if one were all alone ..."

infinitesimal infinitely small

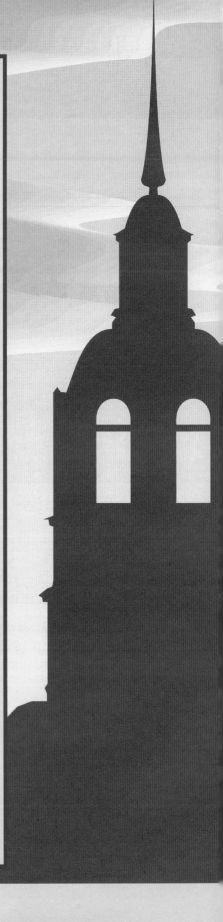

About the text

Frankenstein by Mary Shelley is generally regarded as one of the first science fiction stories. Shelley examines the idea that modern science may be able to create wonders but we are not always aware of the consequences. This is still a very controversial issue – think about the current debate over cloning and test-tube babies.

In this extract, Dr Frankenstein at last sees his creation come to life.

As you read, consider the following features of the text:

Word level

• This is a very descriptive passage. Look closely at the use of adverbs and adjectives.

• *Frankenstein* was published in 1818. Can you find any words or phrases that are no longer commonly used today, or are used in a different way?

Sentence level

• The novel is constructed as the transcript of Frankenstein's speech as he tells his story to a ship's captain. How does Shelley make the writing sound like speech? Look especially at the use of semi-colons and exclamation marks.

• Many of the sentences are very complex. Pick a good example and try writing it in a more modern style as a series of shorter sentences. What is lost or gained?

Text level

• How does Mary Shelley portray Frankenstein's disappointment and horror?

• What do you think is the significance of the dream?

Frankenstein

by Mary Shelley

It was on a dreary night of November that I beheld the accomplishment of my toils. With an anxiety that almost amounted to agony, I collected the instruments of life around me, that I might infuse a spark of being into the lifeless thing that lay at my feet. It was already one in the morning; the rain pattered dismally against the panes, and my candle was nearly burnt out, when, by the glimmer of the half-extinguished light, I saw the dull yellow eye of the creature open; it breathed hard, and a convulsive motion agitated its limbs.

How can I describe my emotions at this catastrophe, or how **delineate** the wretch whom with such infinite pains and care I had endeavoured to form? His limbs were in proportion, and I had selected his features as beautiful. Beautiful! Great God! His yellow skin scarcely covered the work of muscles and arteries beneath; his hair was of a lustrous black, and flowing; his teeth of a pearly whiteness; but these luxuriances only formed a more horrid contrast with his watery eyes, that seemed almost of the same colour as the dun-white sockets in which they were set, his shrivelled complexion and straight black lips.

The different accidents of life are not so changeable as the feelings of human nature. I had worked hard for nearly two years, for the sole purpose of infusing life into an inanimate body. For this I had deprived myself of rest and health. I had desired it with

delineate portray

creating psychological detail **63**

ardour passion

lassitude exhaustion, weariness

Elizabeth Frankenstein's fiancée

livid of a bluish leaden colour, discoloured as by a bruise

an **ardour** that far exceeded moderation; but now that I had finished, the beauty of the dream vanished, and breathless horror and disgust filled my heart. Unable to endure the aspect of the being I had created, I rushed out of the room and continued a long time traversing my bed-chamber, unable to compose my mind to sleep. At length **lassitude** succeeded to the tumult I had before endured, and I threw myself on the bed in my clothes, endeavouring to seek a few moments of forgetfulness. But it was in vain; I slept, indeed, but I was disturbed by the wildest dreams. I thought I saw **Elizabeth**, in the bloom of health, walking in the streets of Ingolstadt. Delighted and surprised, I embraced her, but as I imprinted the first kiss on her lips, they became **livid** with the hue of death; her features appeared to change, and I thought that I held the corpse of my dead mother in my arms; a shroud enveloped her form, and I saw the grave-worms crawling in the folds of the flannel. I started from my sleep with horror; a cold dew covered my forehead, my teeth chattered, and every limb became convulsed; when, by the dim and yellow light of the moon, as it forced its way through the window shutters, I beheld the wretch – the miserable monster whom I had created. He held up the curtain of the bed; and his eyes, if eyes they may be called, were fixed on me. His jaws opened, and he muttered some inarticulate sounds, while a grin wrinkled his cheeks. He might have spoken, but I did not hear; one hand was stretched out, seemingly to detain me, but I escaped and rushed downstairs. I took refuge in the courtyard belonging to the house which I inhabited, where I remained during the rest of the night, walking up and down in the greatest agitation, listening attentively, catching and fearing each sound as if it were to announce the approach of the **demoniacal** corpse to which I had so miserably given life.

Oh! No mortal could support the horror of that countenance. A mummy again **endued** with animation could not be so hideous as that wretch. I had gazed on him while unfinished; he was ugly then, but when those muscles and joints were rendered capable of motion, it became a thing such as even **Dante** could not have conceived.

I passed the night wretchedly. Sometimes my pulse beat so quickly and hardly that I felt the **palpitation** of every artery; at others, I nearly sank to the ground through languor and extreme weakness. Mingled with this horror, I felt the bitterness of disappointment; dreams that had been my food and pleasant rest for so long a space were now become a hell to me; and the change was so rapid, the overthrow so complete!

Morning, dismal and wet, at length dawned and discovered to my sleepless and aching eyes the church of Ingolstadt, its white steeple and clock, which indicated the sixth hour. The porter opened the gates of the court, which had that night been my asylum, and I issued into the streets, pacing them with quick steps, as if I sought to avoid the wretch whom I feared every turning of the street would present to my view.

demoniacal like a demon or devil

endued provided

Dante Italian poet, author of *The Divine Comedy* in which he describes the inhabitants of Inferno (Hell)

palpitation fluttering

creating psychological detail **65**

About the text

Melvyn Burgess is an acclaimed writer of books for teenagers. In *Bloodtide* he imagines a London of the future in which law and order have broken down. The city is controlled by rival families of ganglords, the Volsons and the Conors. Not only that, but genetic mutations have occurred, creating a race of *halfmen*, half-human, half-animal, who live on the outskirts of the city.

In order to cement a truce, Val Volson gives his fourteen-year-old daughter Signy in marriage to Conor. For Signy and her brother, Siggy, this is the start of a violent journey. In this extract, Conor enters the Volson territory to claim his bride.

As you read, consider the following features of the text:

Word level

- Notice how Melvyn Burgess uses mainly familiar vocabulary to persuade us that the London of the future is still recognisable.

Sentence level

- Notice the use of a rhetorical question and *you* to bring the reader into the writing.

- Melvyn Burgess varies the length of his sentences, often using short sentences for emphasis.

Text level

- This episode takes place early on in the novel. How does he get background information across to the reader without detracting from the atmosphere?

- Look at how Burgess uses sound to create atmosphere.

science fiction

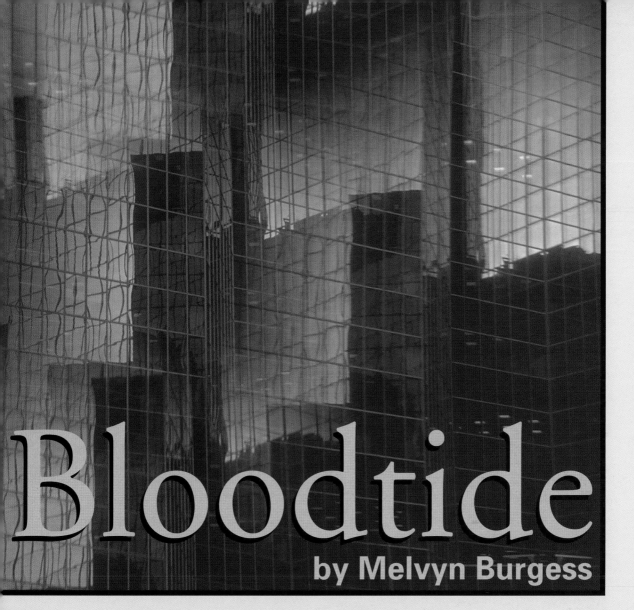

Bloodtide
by Melvyn Burgess

A cold rain whipped between the buildings and across the streets, where a thin, scratty crowd was waiting quietly. Some hid under blankets and umbrellas mended ten times ten, but most of them just stood there soaking. Val was disappointed. He'd wanted the crowds ten deep, cheering and throwing bunting. But he refused to force them.

The bodyguards waited, Val's on this side, Conor's on the other. They wore black suits and let the rain trickle out of their hair and down under their dark glasses. They might have been men, or machines, or animals, or all three. Under their suits you could see the outlines of powerful weapons which may have been part of their bodies.

There had been war between these two families for generations. This was supposed to be a treaty but no one really dared believe it. It was likely just another trick. But who was playing it?

For a long time there was just a low murmur from the crowd and the steady hissing of the rain on the bricks and pavements, but at last a long convoy of cars and armoured vehicles turned into

Bishopsgate and crept over the cracked tarmac. As the sound of the engines grew, there was a strange effect. The hissing began to get louder. The faces of the VIPs turned upwards, looking for the heavy rainfall that must be making the sound, but the rain was falling off if anything. The hissing increased, louder and louder, even over the sound of the engines, as if the rain was insisting on its right to be heard.

It wasn't water; it was people pulling an old schoolboy trick. The thin rows of white faces lifted up from their huddle of rags and bits of plastic to watch an old enemy arrive among them. They didn't dare to boo or shout abuse for fear of Val's gangmen hidden in among them, but no one could tell where the hisses came from. Faces and mouths stayed still as paintings, but hundreds of throats hissed their hatred. The gang wars had crippled London for generations. Conor and his family had fought savagely and cruelly. There wasn't a soul in this crowd who hadn't lost a loved one to the man now driving in to visit them.

The noise began to gather force, to swell. Val was white with rage and frustration, but there was nothing he could do about it. This was his dream! He was putting together the army that was supposed to conquer paradise. These were the people who would break out of the asylum and take the world into the pockets of the poor. The people of the city had shared so many of his dreams, but not this one – not yet.

Conor's convoy, tiny in the shadow of the Galaxy Building, stopped in the square outside and the soldiers emerged from the armoured cars, bristling with weaponry like little toy men in the wide road.

The crowd began hissing again when Conor's personal bodyguard got out of the car. He … it … bared its teeth and its fur stood up on end at the sound until it looked pretty near twice as big. Then it opened its mouth – shouting or barking, who knows. It turned to open the door for Conor.

That was a halfman; Londoners had reason to hate them too, but Conor was the real monster. When he stepped out of his armoured car, the hissing swelled up until it sounded like something was going to burst. Conor pulled his coat around him and looked about as if he stood alone on the rainy street.

Out from among the umbrellas came Val, dressed all in grey, as usual, as if he was someone's clerk. But around his neck he wore a bright crimson silk scarf, as he always did on public appearances. A symbol of fire and blood.

The crowd began to cheer for their leader. They loved Val even more than they hated Conor. But the cheering faltered as Conor and Val embraced each other. A few seconds later, as Val took his daughter in his hand and handed her to Conor, it was in a stony silence. Signy was fourteen years old, and scared white even though she knew how to kill a man. Conor leaned across and kissed her. Among the guard of honour that led between the convoy and the Galaxy Building, Siggy stood with the rain streaming down his face, but he kept so completely still that no one could tell his face was wet with tears.

science fiction

Into the darkness

About the chapter

Readers have always been fascinated by gruesome tales, but it wasn't until the nineteenth century that the horror story as we know it was born. This chapter contains a famous early example of the genre by Bram Stoker as well as more modern stories. Nowadays, we tend to think of film as the definitive form of horror, but, as you will see, writers can still shock us.

horror and the supernatural

About the text

Undoubtedly the most famous horror story ever written, *Dracula* still casts its spell. It seems that the vampire will never die.

Here are two short extracts. In the first, Jonathan Harker, imprisoned in Count Dracula's castle, looks out of a window. What he sees chills his blood.

As you read, consider the following features of the text:

Word level

- This part of the book consists of extracts from Harker's diary. Notice how the language is very straightforward and precise as if he is trying to be calm and rational.

Sentence level

- The sentences are of varying lengths. What effect do the short sentences produce?

- Notice the use of repetition (for example, *I am in fear, awful fear* ...).

- Look closely at the sentence in the second extract beginning, *There, in one of the great boxes* ... . What effect does embedding the subordinate clauses have?

Text level

- Because Harker is the narrator of the story, Bram Stoker makes him appear sane and sensible so that we understand – and also believe – what is happening to him.

- Look at how the Count is revealed in both extracts. How does this create tension?

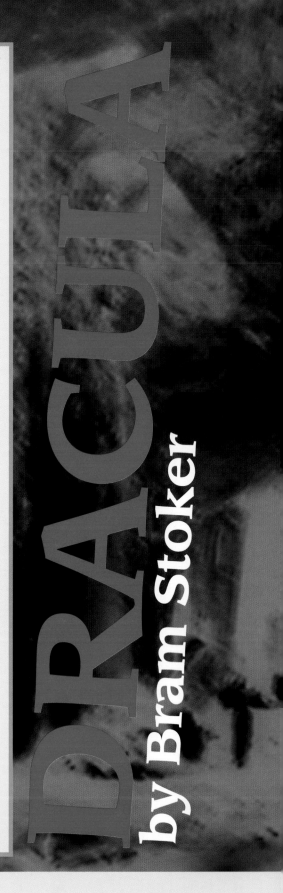

DRACULA
by Bram Stoker

When he left me I went to my room. After a little while, not hearing any sound, I came out and went up the stone stair to where I could look out towards the South. There was some sense of freedom in the vast expanse, inaccessible though it was to me, as compared with the narrow darkness of the courtyard. Looking out on this, I felt that I was indeed in prison, and I seemed to want a breath of fresh air, though it were of the night. I am beginning to feel this nocturnal existence tell on me. It is destroying my nerve. I start at my own shadow, and am full of all sorts of horrible imaginings. God knows that there is ground for any terrible fear in this accursed place! I looked out over the beautiful expanse, bathed in soft yellow moonlight till it was almost as light as day. In the soft light the distant hills became melted, and the shadows in the valleys and gorges of velvety blackness. The mere beauty seemed to cheer me; there was peace and comfort in every breath I drew. As I leaned from the window my eye was caught by something moving a storey below me, and somewhat to my left, where I imagined, from the lie of the rooms, that the windows of the Count's own room would look out. The window at which I stood was tall and deep, stone-**mullioned**, and though weatherworn, was still complete; but it was evidently many a day since the case had been there. I drew back behind the stonework, and looked carefully out.

What I saw was the Count's head coming out from the window. I did not see the face, but I knew the man by the neck and the movement of his back and arms. In any case, I could not mistake the hands which I had had some many opportunities of studying. I was at first interested and somewhat amused, for it is wonderful how small a matter will

mullion vertical bar dividing a window

interest and amuse a man when he is a prisoner. But my very feelings changed to repulsion and terror when I saw the whole man slowly emerge from the window and begin to crawl down the castle wall over the dreadful abyss, *face down*, with his cloak spreading out around him like great wings. At first I could not believe my eyes. I thought it was some trick of the moonlight, some weird effect of shadow; but I kept looking, and it could be no delusion. I saw the fingers and toes grasp the corners of the stones, worn clear of the mortar by the stress of years, and by thus using every projection and inequality move downwards with considerable speed, just as a lizard moves along a wall.

What manner of man is this, or what manner of creature is it in the semblance of man? I feel the dread of this horrible place overpowering me. I am in fear, in awful fear, and there is no escape for me; I am encompassed about with terrors that I dare not think of.

Later in the book, during daylight, Harker manages to climb out of his room and begins to explore the castle.

At one corner of the room was a heavy door. I tried it, for, since I could not find the key of the room or the key of the outer door, which was the main object of my search, I must make further examination, or all my efforts would be in vain. It was open, and led through a stone passage to a circular stairway, which went steeply down. I descended, minding carefully where I went, for the stairs were dark, being only lit by loopholes in the heavy masonry. At the bottom there was a dark, tunnel-like passage, through which came a deathly, sickly odour, the odour of old earth newly turned. As I went through the passage the smell grew closer and heavier. At last I pulled open a heavy door which stood ajar, and found myself in an old, ruined chapel, which had evidently been used as a graveyard. The roof was broken, and in two places were steps leading to vaults, but the ground had recently been dug over, and the earth placed in great wooden boxes, manifestly those which had been brought by the Slovaks. There was nobody about, and I made a search for any further outlet, but there was none. Then I went over every inch of the ground, so as not to lose a chance. I went down even into the vaults, where the dim light struggled, although to do so was a dread to my very soul. Into two of these I went, but saw nothing except fragments of old coffins and piles of dust; in the third, however, I made a discovery.

There, in one of the great boxes, of which there were fifty in all, on a pile of newly dug earth, lay the Count! He was either dead or asleep, I could not say which, for the eyes were open and stony, but without the glassiness of death, and the cheeks had the warmth of life through all their pallor and the lips were as red as ever. But there was no sign of movement, no pulse, no breath, no beating of the heart. I bent over him, and tried to find any sign of life, but in vain. He could not have lain there long, for the earthy smell would have passed away in a few hours. By the side of the box was its cover, pierced with holes here and there. I thought he might have the keys on him, but when I went to search I saw the dead eyes, and in them, dead though they were, such a look of hate, though unconscious of me or my presence, that I fled from the place, and leaving the Count's room by the window, crawled again up the castle wall. Regaining my room, I threw myself panting upon the bed and tried to think.

About the text

This powerful story needs to be read very carefully or you might miss what has really happened.

Important note! Because of the nature of the story, it is better to consider the following points *after* reading it. You might like to cover this box while you read.

Word level

- The language is poetic, creating a dark, tense atmosphere. Which words most contribute to this?

- Note the American spellings of words such as *plowed* and *neighboring*.

Sentence level

- There are some very long sentences. Look at one closely and try to re-punctuate it. What effect does this have?

- Why do you think the story moves between the past and the present tense?

- Pam McNew uses repetition often so that the writing takes on a dream-like quality. Can you find a good example and explain how it works?

Text level

- This story contains a powerful twist. Can you work out where in the story it occurs?

- Why do you think that the narrator can't rest in peace?

A Daughter, Lost

by Pam McNew

Another day and sunset and here is the night; too soon, too close, and all too black, but not for the lack of stars. I shut down the truck, idling eight cylinder engine sliding to a halt at the turn of the key, the flick of a wrist, and immediately, the silence comes rushing at me, screaming at me. I grip the steering wheel, knuckles chalkwhite in the darkness, gripping it like it's the tail end of the robe of Jesus, gripping it and holding on, holding on because if I don't let go maybe the darkness and the silence won't become a child, my child, my Ginny who calls to me, who calls and haunts me, her daddy.

I don't look toward the house, red brick farm house without the farm, rural trend because the city is no place to raise a child, raise children, and because Ginny's mother wanted it that way. Old farmhouse built for families with strong sons and determined daughters and their wives and husbands and they would all live atop one another and the fields would get plowed and the hogs slopped and the table would be laid with three meals a day, raised from the fields, from the land itself, planted or bred, sprung, harvested or slaughtered right there on their land, their farm, until the sun burnt the fields and the livestock aged or died for the table, and all that was left was an auction.

"Buy it," my wife said. Buy it for us, she meant. So I did, the house, a couple of outbuildings, enough land to put the wooden-framed swing and slide, the lacy-trimmed princess playhouse, the bicycles of pink and white or purple and white but always with sparkles and tassels for the imagination of a little girl surrounded by cornfields.

I bought it, but never mind the drive for me. Country to city. City to country. Day after day. Driving. Driving countless miles and more countless miles. Then, more work, more time at work. Work, work, work. Until I am tired, tired, tired and can't see straight, can't think straight, can't drive straight, but they wanted to see that Disney movie on a Friday night anyway.

The truck, with the threesome in the front, crashed.

Not everyone survived.

And Ginny haunts me.

Perhaps it is safe. I hear crickets and **katydids** and somewhere on a neighboring farm cattle are too restless to sleep. From truck to house fifty feet. If I hurry, if I quickly leave the truck and quicken my step, perhaps I can make it. Make it to the house, into the house. Join my wife waiting there inside. If she is sleeping and all too often she is sleeping, I will eat a cold dinner in cold silence in cold white light and try not to think of what is outside in the dark. Fifty steps. I loosen my hold on the steering wheel, reach for the door handle, and hold my breath.

Crickets, katydids, cattle. And one lone dog somewhere. Barking. Howling.

I open the door. Quickly now, fifty steps. The bicycles are gone. The playhouse only a black silhouette that I refuse to see, refuse to recognize. Then, there's the playset. The sleek, shiny slide. She hadn't even worn the shine off it, but the swings, she had loved the swings. And one of them is moving, moving back and forth, and I look away, quicken my step. Someone is in that swing, a ghost child, my Ginny in that swing, and the house, the house must be close, close so I hurry, but not fast enough because I hear her voice, I hear Ginny's voice. "Daddy."

I begin to run, run for the house, the door, the white light inside.

"Daddy."

katydid green grasshopper

I'm running, but where is the house? Ginny's voice sounds closer now. I'm running harder, heart pounding, feet pounding, but it's not the pathway that I feel under them. Long grass, and I must have gotten turned around, and I am running the wrong way, towards the fields, Autumn's barren fields, and still I hear Ginny calling me. My feet pounding dirt and cornstalk stubble now, but still running, running, running.

I turn, small turn, positive that Ginny, my child, my ghost child, is behind me, after me, but my foot catches on a stalk or a clump of dirt and I'm falling, falling, falling. Falling not to Earth, but into the heavens. I am falling into a thousand stars.

As I fall, I weep. I weep – weeping, crying, sobbing like a child myself. The stars are forever. The heavens are forever. And then, Ginny is beside me, kneeling beside me as I come to rest. Pale ghostly Ginny, only she's all grown up now. So beautiful, so very beautiful, but translucent, pale, almost invisible.

"Oh, Daddy," she says and she's placing flowers, waxy white blooms with midnight black stems and leaves, above my head. "Oh, Daddy," she says and she sounds so very sad, so very, very sad. "Daddy, won't you ever rest in peace?"

And I close my eyes, like I closed my eyes so many years ago, not intentionally, truly believing I was driving, dreaming I was driving, and the truck, with its humming eight cylinders, left the road, rolled three times, crashed, and not everyone survived.

"Rest in peace, Daddy," my Ginny says and the darkness surrounds me once again.

The darkness surrounds me, but not for the lack of stars.

About the text

Alice Walker is an African-American writer who became well known when her novel *The Color Purple* was published and then filmed by Steven Spielberg. In this very short story, she uses the techniques of the horror genre to portray the terror of racial prejudice.

Important note! Because of the nature of the story, it is better to consider the following points *after* reading it. You might like to cover this box while you read.

Word level

- The story begins like a fairytale or a children's story. How does the choice of language produce this effect?

- Myop is an unusual name. Could it refer to myopia – short-sightedness?

Sentence level

- What is the effect of the final sentence, printed on its own?

Text level

- How do we know that Myop is black?

- Look at the way in which Alice Walker makes the atmosphere darker as the story progresses. In which paragraph do you think this starts to happen?

- How does she reveal the skull?

- Do you think that Myop understands the significance of what she has found? What evidence can you find to back up your view?

The *Flowers*

by Alice Walker

It seemed to Myop as she skipped lightly from hen house to pigpen to smokehouse that the days had never been as beautiful as these. The air held a keenness that made her nose twitch. The harvesting of the corn and cotton, peanuts and squash, made each day a golden surprise that caused excited little tremors to run up her jaws.

Myop carried a short, knobby stick. She struck out at random at chickens she liked, and worked out the beat of a song on the fence around the pigpen. She felt light and good in the warm sun. She was ten, and nothing existed for her but her song, the stick clutched in her dark brown hand, and the tat-de-ta-ta-ta of accompaniment.

Turning her back on the rusty boards of her family's sharecropper cabin, Myop walked along the fence till it ran into the stream made by the spring. Around the spring, where the family got drinking water, silver ferns and wildflowers grew. Along the shallow banks pigs rooted. Myop watched the tiny white bubbles disrupt the thin black scale of soil and the water that silently rose and slid away down the stream.

She had explored the woods behind the house many times. Often, in late autumn, her mother took her to gather nuts among the fallen leaves. Today she made her own path, bouncing this way and that way, vaguely keeping an eye out for snakes. She found, in addition to various common but pretty ferns and leaves, an armful of strange blue flowers with velvety ridges and a sweetsuds bush full of the brown, fragrant buds.

By twelve o'clock, her arms laden with sprigs of her findings, she was a mile or more from home. She had often been as far before, but the strangeness of the land made it not as pleasant as her usual haunts. It seemed gloomy in the little cove in which she found herself. The air was damp, the silence close and deep.

Myop began to circle back to the house, back to the peacefulness of the morning. It was then she stepped smack into his eyes. Her heel became lodged in the broken ridge between brow and nose, and she reached down quickly, unafraid, to free herself. It was only when she saw his naked grin that she gave a little yelp of surprise.

He had been a tall man. From feet to neck covered a long space. His head lay beside him. When she pushed back the leaves and layers of earth and debris Myop saw that he'd had large white teeth, all of them cracked or broken, long fingers, and very big bones. All his clothes had rotted away except some threads of blue denim from his overalls. The buckles of the overalls had turned green.

Myop gazed around the spot with interest. Very near where she'd stepped into the head was a wild pink rose. As she picked it to add to her bundle she noticed a raised mound, a ring, around the rose's root. It was the rotted remains of a **noose**, a bit of shredding plowline, now blending **benignly** into the soil. Around an overhanging limb of a great spreading oak clung another piece. Frayed, rotted, bleached, and frazzled – barely there – but spinning restlessly in the breeze. Myop laid down her flowers.

And the summer was over.

noose rope tied in a loop used for hanging someone

benignly gently, mildly, kindly

The search for love

About the chapter

Romantic fiction is enormously popular, especially among female readers. The style is often parodied but, in exploring the relationship between men and women, the genre can also provide examples of intelligent, sensitive and funny writing. The chapter starts with an extract from Jane Austen's *Persuasion* and ends with a passage from *Bridget Jones's Diary*.

romance

About the text

Jane Austen was among the first professional female novelists. Enormously popular in her day, she is still widely read across the world.

This extract is taken from *Persuasion*, completed in 1816. Anne Elliot is in Lyme Regis visiting friends. While there she meets Captain Wentworth, a man whose proposal of marriage she rejected before the start of the novel. Wentworth is now courting Louisa Musgrove, a very different girl from the sensible Anne.

As you read, consider the following features of the text:

Word level

- Written in the early nineteenth century, *Persuasion* contains many words and phrases that have since become less common or changed their meaning. Choose a sentence or short paragraph and modernise it.

Sentence level

- Jane Austen uses semicolons to break up complex sentences. Look at the paragraph beginning, *He advised against it ...* on page 83. It consists of a single sentence! What effect does this have?

Text level

- Note how, although this extract is all action, we sense a relationship developing between Anne and Captain Wentworth. How is this done?

- Captain Wentworth and Anne are very different in character. How would you describe them?

- Jane Austen uses gentle humour to comment on the events. Can you find some examples?

Persuasion

by Jane Austen

There was too much wind to make the high part of the new **Cobb** pleasant for the ladies, and they agreed to get down the steps to the lower, and all were contented to pass quietly and carefully down the steep flight, excepting Louisa; she must be jumped down them by Captain Wentworth. In all their walks, he had had to jump her from the stiles; the sensation was delightful to her. The hardness of the pavement for her feet, made him less willing upon the present occasion; he did it, however; she was safely down, and instantly, to show her enjoyment, ran up the steps to be jumped down again.

He advised her against it, thought the jar too great; but no, he reasoned and talked in vain; she smiled and said, "I am determined I will:" he put out his hands; she was too **precipitate** by half a second, she fell on the pavement on the Lower Cobb, and was taken up lifeless!

There was no wound, no blood, no visible bruise; but her eyes were closed, she breathed not, her face was like death. The horror of the moment to all who stood around!

Captain Wentworth, who had caught her up, knelt with her in his arms, looking on her with a face as pallid as her own, in an agony of silence.

"She is dead! she is dead!" screamed Mary, catching hold of her husband, and contributing with his own horror to make him immoveable; and in another moment, Henrietta, sinking under the conviction, lost her senses too, and would have fallen on the steps, but for Captain Benwick and Anne, who caught and supported her between them.

"Is there no one to help me?" were the first words which burst from Captain Wentworth, in a tone of despair, and as if all his own strength were gone.

"Go to him, go to him," cried Anne, "for heaven's sake go to him. I can support her myself. Leave me, and go to him. Rub her hands, rub her temples; here are salts; take them, take them."

Captain Benwick obeyed, and Charles at the same moment, disengaging himself from his wife, they were both with him; and Louisa was raised up and

the Cobb a stone harbour wall, jutting out into the sea

precipitate hasty, rash

portraying emotion in action

supported more firmly between them, and everything was done that Anne had prompted, but in vain; while Captain Wentworth, staggering against the wall for his support, exclaimed in the bitterest agony –

"Oh God! her father and mother!"

"A surgeon!" said Anne.

He caught the word; it seemed to rouse him at once, and saying only –

"True, true, a surgeon this instant," was darting away, when Anne eagerly suggested –

"Captain Benwick, would not it be better for Captain Benwick? He knows where a surgeon is to be found."

Every one capable of thinking felt the advantage of the idea, and in a moment (it was all done in rapid moments) Captain Benwick had resigned the poor corpse-like figure entirely to the brother's care, and was off for the town with the utmost rapidity.

As to the wretched party left behind, it could scarcely be said which of the three, who were completely rational, was suffering most: Captain Wentworth, Anne, or Charles, who, really a very affectionate brother, hung over Louisa with sobs of grief, and could only turn his eyes from one sister, to see the other in a state as insensible, or to witness the hysterical agitations of his wife, calling on him for help which he could not give.

Anne, attending with all the strength and zeal, and thought, which instinct supplied, to Henrietta, still tried, at intervals, to suggest comfort to the others, tried to quiet Mary, to animate Charles, to **assuage** the feelings of Captain Wentworth. Both seemed to look to her for directions.

"Anne, Anne," cried Charles, "What is to be done next? What, in heaven's name, is to be done next?"

Captain Wentworth's eyes were also turned towards her.

"Had not she better be carried to the inn? Yes, I am sure: carry her gently to the inn."

"Yes, yes, to the inn," repeated Captain Wentworth, comparatively collected, and eager to be doing something. "I will carry her myself. Musgrove, take care of the others."

By this time the report of the accident had spread among the workmen and boatmen about the Cobb, and many were collected near them, to be useful if

assuage calm, soothe

wanted, at any rate, to enjoy the sight of a dead young lady, nay, two dead young ladies, for it proved twice as fine as the first report. To some of the best-looking of these good people Henrietta was consigned, for, though partially revived, she was quite helpless; and in this manner, Anne walking by her side, and Charles attending to his wife, they set forward, treading back with feelings unutterable, the ground, which so lately, so very lately, and so light of heart, they had passed along.

They were not off the Cobb, before the Harvilles met them. Captain Benwick had been seen flying by their house, with a countenance which showed something to be wrong; and they had set off immediately, informed and directed as they passed, towards the spot. Shocked as Captain Harville was, he brought senses and nerves that could be instantly useful; and a look between him and his wife decided what was to be done. She must be taken to their house; all must go to their house; and await the surgeon's arrival there. They would not listen to **scruples**: he was obeyed; they were all beneath his roof; and while Louisa, under Mrs Harville's direction, was conveyed up stairs, and given possession of her own bed, assistance, cordials, restoratives were supplied by her husband to all who needed them.

Louisa had once opened her eyes, but soon closed them again, without apparent consciousness. This had been a proof of life, however, of service to her sister; and Henrietta, though perfectly incapable of being in the same room with Louisa, was kept, by the agitation of hope and fear, from a return of her own insensibility. Mary, too, was growing calmer.

The surgeon was with them almost before it had seemed possible. They were sick with horror, while he examined; but he was not hopeless. The head had received a severe **contusion**, but he had seen greater injuries recovered from: he was by no means hopeless; he spoke cheerfully.

That he did not regard it as a desperate case, that he did not say a few hours must end it, was at first felt, beyond the hope of most; and the ecstasy of such a reprieve, the rejoicing, deep and silent, after a few fervent ejaculations of gratitude to Heaven had been offered, may be conceived.

The tone, the look, with which "Thank God!" was uttered by Captain Wentworth, Anne was sure could never be forgotten by her; nor the sight of him afterwards, as he sat near a table, leaning over it with folded arms and face concealed, as if overpowered by the various feelings of his soul, and trying by prayer and reflection to calm them.

scruples doubts, hesitation

contusion blow to the body, bruise

About the text

Kiss and Tell is a good example of contemporary romantic fiction. The hero, Jake Dolan, is a secret agent hiding away from the world in a high-security underground compound, trying to work out who double-crossed him. One day his isolation is shattered by the arrival of Marnie Wright.

As you read, consider the following features of the text:

Word level

- The writing is very descriptive. Look carefully at the writer's choice of adjectives, adverbs and verbs.

- The language is colloquial and uses everyday American slang or idiom. Note too the American spellings of words such as *humor* and *color*.

Sentence level

- Note the use of short sentences to heighten tension.

Text level

- Interestingly, we see Marnie through Jake's eyes and Jake through Marnie's. Marnie's view is given greater weight, though. Why do you think this is?

- As is often the case with romance, the couple are antagonistic to start with.

- Note how the writer uses the dog to bring the couple together.

- The writing is often humorous, using sarcasm and an ironic tone.

KISS AND TELL

by Cherry Adair

The perimeter alarms were set to go off when anything heavier than a hundred pounds crossed the almost invisible breakers. At first all Jake saw on the monitor was the fawn-colored Great Dane. The damn thing was a mean-looking bastard and as big as a house.

"Where the hell did you come from?"

The dog's large, square head and pointy ears swivelled, as if it could smell him down here, twenty feet below ground level. Jake stuck his size fourteens up on the counter and took another swig of soda. His eyes narrowed as he scrutinized the flat-screen monitor before him.

A second later his feet dropped to the floor at the same time his fist crushed the empty can. "S**t."

The dog had been hiding her.

For a split second …

Jake absently touched the scar on his throat, and ignored the from zero-to-eighty acceleration of his blood pressure. He leaned forward to adjust the focus and shifted closer to get a better look.

A slender blonde, drowning in a green down jacket, sat not thirty feet from the front door of his cabin on the tree uprooted by last year's storm. Fair hair, all the colors of the sun and fingered by the breeze, danced in joyous spiral curls around her face and hunched shoulders as she concentrated on something in her lap.

Her skin was fair instead of dusky, her hair silky, not coarse, the angle of her head unfamiliar. She was no ghost from the past. Thank God.

Nevertheless, he didn't want her here.

Jake didn't know who she was or what she was doing in the high, remote Sierras at the nose of winter. Her mere presence was suspect. Not that she appeared to be anything other than a cute blonde on a solitary mountain hike. But then looks could be deceiving.

Neither the girl nor the dog was welcome.

He didn't like dogs. In his line of work they tended to be unpredictable. As for the fluffy blonde … . Jake slam-dunked the squashed can into the trash, then leaned forward for a better look. He definitely didn't like that breed, either.

Closer inspection didn't improve her one bit. Unfortunately he hadn't had a woman in nearly a year, and this cupcake made his mouth water. Too bad. Like a mouse to an elephant, like David to Goliath. She was exactly the type of woman he avoided like the plague – petite, blonde, and delicate.

He was bone exhausted from an assignment in a small, forgotten Middle Eastern country where all hell had broken loose. All he'd wanted to do was take a break. Instead he'd come home to find the s**t hitting the fan, his sixteen-year career in the toilet, and the vacation he'd wanted being enforced.

He had no time for the blonde outside.

Most likely a strong "boo" would send girl and hound running for town. After they left he'd get back to figuring out who was screwing with his life.

★ ★ ★

Marnie Wright wished she'd brought along a warm cap. Cold air nipped at her ears, making them sting. Dismissing the discomfort, she focused on the sketch pad on her lap.

It had been a bonus finding this old cottage tucked into the hillside. She'd hate to waste the light walking the mile back to her grandmother's cottage just because she was cold. She flipped up her collar and hunched her shoulders.

Only the front walls and the peak of the shingled roof showed through the surrounding trees, shrubs, and piles of deadfall. It was in better shape than Grammy's. While rustic, the wood siding and front porch had recently been repaired. The roof appeared solid, the windows intact.

Marnie flexed her fingers, narrowing her eyes at the log cabin before she continued drawing. The little house was perfect for the creepy Halloween story she was working on. All it needed was a little atmosphere. She shaded a curved whisper of smoke above the chimney, elongating dark shadows to make the small house unwelcoming and sinister. The fluid black lines of her charcoal pencil skimmed the page. Beside her, Duchess's head swivelled.

"What're you listening to? A chipmunk?"

Her dog made a low sound in her throat and wagged her tail.

Marnie laughed, her breath misting in the frigid air. "Don't go far." She put her hand behind her pet's massive head and looked her sternly in the eye. "And don't play with it, you hear me?"

Duchess bounded to the closed door of the empty cottage. She settled her backside on the front step, ears perked. Marnie smiled. Duchess loved her creature comforts. Rather than frolic about in the cold, she wanted inside.

"That's not home, doofus. Give me a few more minutes and we'll pack up and go, okay?"

She had lugged her sleeping bag and supplies to her grandmother's cottage before she and Duchess had taken a stroll, ending up at this isolated place. The exercise, and the cold, had made her hungry, too. She smelled rain and wanted to be back before it started pouring.

With a frown she considered for half a second going home to Sunnyvale. The river had a tendency to flood, making the bridge impassable. Leaving would be the prudent, safe thing to do.

But she didn't want to be prudent and sensible anymore. The decisions and choices she made in the next couple of days were going to change her future. After a lifetime of playing it safe, she needed to learn to take the chances life presented her.

Some of her happiest memories had been made up here at Grammy's cottage. And here was where she was going to decide the course of the rest of her life. A little rain wasn't going to

deter her.

She'd almost forgotten what a pain in the butt it was to get up here. She'd left her car at the end of the narrow mountain road, then crossed the skinny footbridge fording the river, passed over another bridge spanning the ravine, and then had a three-mile hike up the mountainside. As kids, she and her brothers hadn't noticed such minor inconveniences. It had always been a grand adventure to come here with Grammy. They'd explored every inch of the mountain, played in the river, and climbed the trees like monkeys.

A little rain and cold wouldn't hurt. This was probably the last time she'd …

A twig snapped behind her. The pencil jerked in her hand, leaving a jagged

smear across the paper. Marnie froze. She looked at Duchess. The animal shifted impatiently on the front porch of the little cottage, brow furrowed, ears rotating like radar. Marnie's shoulders relaxed.

For half a second.

"This is private property."

Her head shot up, and she looked over her shoulder.

He stood slightly to the left and behind her, as big as a mountain and impossible to miss. Why hadn't Duchess raced up to protect her, as she usually did? And how had he walked up this close without her hearing him? And he was close. He stood with booted feet spread, a shotgun cradled casually in the crook of his arm.

Dark hair hung to his massive shoulders. Heavy five o'clock shadow blurred his features. Tall and broad-shouldered, he was dressed in jeans and covered to mid thigh by a thick down jacket similar to her own. He looked like something out of Soldier of Fortune magazine, only a great deal less friendly.

"Where'd you come from?" Marnie asked brightly, flipping the cardboard cover over the sketch pad in her lap. She gathered her wits and braced her feet in preparation for quick action if it became necessary.

"Who are you, and what are you doing here?"

"Marnie Wright. I'm visiting– I'm– I'm just here," she finished in exasperation. I'm here to rethink my life. I'm here to contemplate my future. I wasn't expecting the Incredible Hulk!

"There isn't anyone else up here. Just who are you supposed to be visiting?"

"I'm visiting my grandmother's old cottage. It's down there." Marnie pointed down the hill. "She–"

"Are you alone?"

She wasn't stupid. "I'm expecting company later. Soon."

"Meet your company across the bridge."

Instead of his rudeness putting her off, Marnie was intrigued. "Who are you?" she asked curiously. "And what are you doing here at this time of year?"

"Lady, this isn't a goddamn cocktail

party. Forget the chitchat and get lost." His lips thinned to a hard line. "Take the dog and move out."

"Move out?" Marnie cocked her head and pulled the canvas bag into her lap. Military, for sure. She definitely knew the type. Her brother Michael was a navy **SEAL**.

Unfortunately for this guy, she was sick and tired of being told what to do, and when to do it, by bossy men. She was pretty sure he wouldn't shoot her. In the meantime she was perfectly happy where she was, thank you very much. She gave him a **limpid** look.

He repeated his words in French, then in German, just in case she didn't get the message. His deep baritone stroked across her imagination, shimmied through her bones. The quiet tone, deep and compelling, rough with impatience, made her shiver.

This was a man used to giving commands and receiving immediate obedience. His gaze slid downward over her open jacket, purple sweatshirt, well-worn jeans, and heavy hiking boots, then slowly back up again.

Marnie trembled as if he'd physically touched her.

He had remarkable eyes – a mesmerizing, unfriendly dark blue. He scrutinized her with an intensity usually reserved for particularly dangerous reptiles. He held her gaze as he strode around the exposed roots of the tree until he stood before her. Considerably more intimidating head on, he had a straight nose and heavy eyebrows, one of which was bisected by a thin white scar – A scar more recent than childhood. The man was a fighter. Beneath the blur of dark facial hair she detected a square, stubborn chin.

And the sexiest mouth …

His nearness unsettled her to the core. But that had nothing to do with his attitude. She had four brothers who could appear just as intimidating. She'd been raised around men, but she'd never had this sort of immediate reaction. Her knee-jerk response to him unnerved her.

He glared, then said, as well as signed, "Are you deaf, woman?"

Marnie's gaze flickered from the movement of his large, expressive hands back to his scowling face. She felt a leap of interest, a spark of excitement, a frisson of searing attraction as he stood there glaring down at her.

Lust at first sight.

SEAL commando, member of a Sea, Air and Land Team

limpid clear, comprehensible

She sighed.

Lust was wholly inappropriate reaction considering the circumstances. She held his gaze, one eyebrow raised in query at his threatening stance. He was a huge man, taller than her five-six by almost a foot. A warning glittered from narrowed eyes, his hostility meant to scare away even the most intrepid. The shotgun was overkill.

"I'd be able to hear you even if you weren't yelling."

"Then what part of 'get lost' don't you understand?"

"It's a big mountain. I'm not taking up much room, am I?"

Not taking her eyes off him, she rested her hand lightly on her day pack. Besides her art supplies, she carried a can of Mace and a roll of

quarters knotted in an old knee-high stocking. A girl could never be too prepared. Unfortunately, she had a feeling neither her makeshift weapon, nor her yellow belt in Aikido, would make a dent in this guy. Part of her wondered at her **temerity** baiting this angry stranger. The part that was fascinated made her stay put.

In her peripheral vision, she saw Duchess directly behind him. The dog stood four square, staring at his back, a sappy, slobbery grin on her canine face.

"This might be a big mountain, but this is my little chunk, and I like it just fine without you on it. Move, lady."

"Sorry, I'm not ready to move yet."

She tried the fluttering eyelash thing that worked with her brothers, knowing she was playing with fire, and enjoying it immensely.

"Honest, I'm harmless. All I'm doing is drawing the cottage for a book I'm illus–"

"Lady, I don't give a damn if you're Picasso. The cabin belongs to me. The tree you're sitting on belongs to me, and the damn land you're on belongs to me. Haul your butt and your dog off my property."

"Well, since you put it so nicely …"

More amused by his annoyance than afraid, she smiled up at him. There

temerity excessive confidence

romance

wasn't a trace of indulgent humor in those dark, glacial eyes. He obviously didn't find her as cute and adorable as her brothers did.

He scowled. "Are you as stupid as you look?"

"That's kind of like asking the man if he's stopped beating his wife, isn't it?" Marnie stood, dusting moss and bits of bark off her behind. Darn. Her butt was damp. "Are you always this rude to strangers?"

Duchess walked daintily around him, coming to her side and leaning her enormous head against Marnie's arm.

"Lady." Obviously exasperated, he clicked the safety off the gun. Her shoulders stiffened. "What the hell do I have to do to get you off this mountain? Shoot you?"

"Jeez, keep your shirt on. I'm going already!" She picked up the pencils that had rolled to the ground when she'd stood, then slipped icy fingers beneath Duchess's collar.

"Come on, sweetheart." She managed to take two steps before she realized that Duchess wasn't moving. "Come on, girl."

Duchess shook off her restraint. For a moment Marnie hoped her dog wasn't going for Mountain Man's throat. She had to choke back a laugh as Duchess wagged her tail, stuffed her head under his free hand, and gazed up at him adoringly.

By his expression she could tell he was not a happy camper. She bit her lip; this was no time to smile. Duchess gave her mistress a soulful look. Marnie made a subtle "stay" hand gesture and the dog leaned against a very large masculine thigh, and heaved an enormous sigh.

"What the hell is this animal doing?"

Marnie's feet scuffed up damp leaves as she strolled away without looking back.

"She likes you." She had to raise her voice to be heard as she put some distance between them.

"Damn it, I told you to – stop that, dog! – take your dog."

"Oh, Duchess goes exactly where she wants. Never have been able to make her come when she wants to stay." She glanced over her shoulder. Duchess was looking up at him as if he were God's gift.

Marnie started to laugh.

About the text

Originally a newspaper column in *The Independent*, *Bridget Jones's Diary* became a publishing phenomenon.

Bridget is a twenty-something professional woman, obsessed with her figure and finding the right man.

On 29 July, she goes to a 'tarts and vicars' party dressed as a bunny-girl, only to find out that she is the only one in fancy dress. To save embarrassment, she is given a hideous bridesmaid's dress to wear. After this disaster, she decides to visit her boyfriend for a bit of moral support.

As you read, consider the following features of the text:

Word level

- The language is straightforward and chatty as you would expect in a diary. Note, though, that Bridget uses some more literary words and phrases (for example, *emboldened*, *human habitation*). What effect do these have?

Sentence level

- Look at the section beginning, *For God's sake ...* towards the end of page 98. Note how the writer uses sentence structure to create tension by delaying information. This is especially effective in the last paragraph where the narration is inserted into the woman's speech.

Text level

- This extract relies on humour to make us feel sympathy for Bridget. She often comments on her own behaviour in a self-critical way. Can you find examples?

- How does Helen Fielding deliberately mislead the reader on page 97?

Bridget Jones's Diary

by Helen Fielding

By the time I got back to London and off the motorway I was feeling pretty shaky and back much earlier than I expected, so I thought, instead of going straight home, I'd go round to Daniel's for a bit of reassurance.

I parked nose to nose with Daniel's car. There was no answer when I rang, so I left it a while and rang again in case it was just in the middle of a really good wicket or something. Still no answer. I knew he must be around because his car was there and he'd said he was going to be working and watching the cricket. I looked up at his window and there was Daniel. I beamed at him, waved and pointed at the door. He disappeared, I assumed to press the buzzer, so I rang the bell again. He took a bit of time to answer: 'Hi, Bridge. Just on the phone to America. Can I meet you in the pub in ten minutes?'

'OK,' I said cheerfully, without thinking, and set off towards the corner. But when I looked round, there he was again, not on the phone, but watching me out of the window.

Cunning as a fox, I pretended not to see and kept walking, but inside I was in turmoil. Why was he watching? Why hadn't he answered the door first time? Why didn't he just press the buzzer and let me come up straight away? Suddenly it hit me like a thunderbolt. He was with a woman.

My heart pounding, I rounded the corner, then, keeping flat against the wall, I peered round to check he had gone from the window. No sign of him. I hurried back and assumed a crouching position in the porch next to his, observing his doorway between the pillars in case a woman came out. I waited, crouched in the position for some time. But then I started to think: if a woman did come out, how would I know it was Daniel's flat she had come out of and not one of the other flats in the building? What would I do? Challenge her? Make a citizen's arrest? Also, what was to stop him leaving the woman in the flat with instructions to stay there until he had had time to get to the pub?

I looked at my watch. 6.30. Hah! The pub wasn't open yet. Perfect excuse. Emboldened, I hurried back towards the door and pushed the buzzer.

'Bridget, is that you again?' he snapped.

'The pub isn't open yet.'

There was silence. Did I hear a voice in the background? In denial, I told myself he was just laundering money or dealing in drugs. He was probably trying to hide polythene bags full of cocaine under the floorboards helped by some smooth South American men with ponytails.

'Let me in,' I said.

'I told you, I'm on the phone.'

'Let me in.'

'What?' He was playing for time, I could tell.

'Press the buzzer, Daniel,' I said.

Isn't it funny how you can detect someone's presence, even though you can't see, hear or otherwise discern them? Oh, of *course* I'd checked the cupboards on the way up on the stairs and there was no one in any of them. But I knew there was a woman in Daniel's house. Maybe it was a slight smell ... something about the way Daniel was behaving. Whatever it was, I just *knew*.

We stood there warily at opposite sides of the sitting room. I was just desperate to start running around opening and closing all the cupboards like my mother and ringing 1471 to see if there was a number stored from America.

'What have you got on?' he said. I had forgotten about Janine's outfit in the excitement.

'A bridesmaid's dress,' I said haughtily.

'Would you like a drink?' said Daniel. I thought fast. I needed to get him into the kitchen so I could go through all the cupboards.

'A cup of tea, please.'

'Are you all right?' he said.

'Yes! Fine!' I trilled. 'Marvellous time at the party. Only one dressed as a tart, had to put on a bridesmaid dress, Mark Darcy was there with Natasha, that's a nice shirt you're wearing ... .' I stopped, out of breath, realizing I had turned (there was no 'was turning' about it) into my mother.

He looked at me for a moment, then set off into the kitchen at which I quickly leapt across the room to look behind the sofa and the curtains.

'What are you doing?'

'Nothing, nothing. Just thought I might have left a skirt of mine behind the sofa,' I said, wildly plumping up the cushions as if I were in a French farce.

He looked suspicious and headed off to the kitchen again.

Deciding there was no time to dial 1471, I quickly checked the cupboard where he keeps the duvet for the sofabed – no human habitation – then followed him to the kitchen, pulling open the door of the hall cupboard as I passed at which the ironing board fell out, followed by a cardboard box full of old **45s** which slithered out all over the floor.

'What are you doing?' said Daniel mildly again, coming out of the kitchen.

'Sorry, just caught the door with my sleeve,' I said. 'Just on my way to the loo.'

Daniel was staring at me as if I was mad, so I couldn't go and check the bedroom. Instead I locked the loo door and started frantically looking around for things. I wasn't exactly sure what, but long blonde hairs, tissues with lipstick marks on, alien hairbrushes – any of these would have been a sign. Nothing. Next I quietly unlocked the door, looked both ways, slipped along the corridor, pushed open the door of Daniel's bedroom and nearly jumped out of my skin. There was someone in the room.

'Bridge.' It was Daniel, defensively holding a pair of jeans in front of him. 'What are you doing in here?

'I heard you come in here so ... I thought ... it was a secret **assignation**,' I said, approaching him in what would have been a sexy way were it not for the floral sprig dress. I leaned my head on his chest and put my arms around him, trying to smell his shirt for perfume traces and get a good look at the bed, which was unmade as usual.

'Mmmmm, you've still got the bunny girl outfit on underneath, haven't you?' he said, starting to unzip the bridesmaid dress and pressing against me in a way which made his intentions very clear. I suddenly thought this might be a trick and he was going to seduce me while the woman slipped out unnoticed.

'Oooh, the kettle must be boiling,' said Daniel suddenly, zipping my dress up again and patting me reassuringly in a way that was most unlike him. Usually once he gets going he will see things through to their logical conclusion come earthquake, tidal wave or naked pictures of **Virginia Bottomley** on the television.

'Ooh yes, better make that cuppa,' I said, thinking it would give me a chance to get a good look round the bedroom and scout the study.

'After you,' said Daniel, pushing me out and shutting the door so I had to walk ahead of him back into the kitchen. As I did so I suddenly caught sight of the door that led to the roof terrace.

'Shall we go and sit down?' said Daniel.

That was where she was, she was on the bloody roof.

'What's the matter with you?'

45s a vinyl record played at 45rpm, a single

assignation a secret appointment between lovers

Virginia Bottomley Conservative MP

he said as I stared at the door suspiciously.

'No-thing,' I sing-songed gaily, flopping into the sitting room. 'Just a little tired from the party.'

I flung myself **insouciantly** on to the sofa, wondering whether to streak faster than the speed of light down to the study as the final place she might be or just go hell for leather for the roof. I figured if she wasn't on the roof it meant she must be in the study, in the bedroom wardrobe, or under the bed. If we then went up on the roof she would be able to escape. But if that was the case, surely Daniel would have suggested going up on the roof much sooner.

He brought me a cup of tea and sat down at his laptop, which was open and turned on. Only then did I start to think that maybe there was no woman. There was a document up on the screen – maybe he really had been working and on the phone to America. And I was making a complete prat of myself behaving like a madwoman.

'Are you sure everything's all right, Bridge?'

'Fine, yes. Why?'

'Well, coming round unannounced like this dressed as a rabbit disguised as a bridesmaid and burrowing into all the rooms in a strange way. Not meaning to pry or anything, I just wondered if there was an explanation, that's all.'

I felt a complete fool. It was bloody Mark Darcy trying to wreck my relationship by sowing suspicions in my mind. Poor Daniel, it was so unfair to doubt him in this way, because of the word of some arrogant, ill-tempered, top-flight human-rights lawyer. Then I heard a scraping noise on the roof above us.

'I think maybe I'm just a bit hot,' I said, watching Daniel carefully. 'I think maybe I'll go and sit on the roof for a while.'

'For God's sake, will you sit still for two minutes!' he yelled, moving to bar my path, but I was too quick for him. I dodged past, opened the door, ran up the stairs and opened the hatch out into the sunlight.

There, spread out on a sunlounger, was a bronzed, long-limbed, blonde-haired stark-naked woman. I stood there frozen to the spot, feeling like an enormous pudding in the bridesmaid dress. The woman raised her head, lifted her sunglasses and looked at me with one eye closed. I heard Daniel coming up the stairs behind me.

'Honey,' said the woman, in an American accent, looking over my head at him. 'I thought you said she was *thin*.'

---

insouciantly in a carefree manner, unconcerned

6

Crime and punishment

About the chapter

Since the invention of the police, readers have been fascinated by the detection of crime. This chapter covers many aspects of crime fiction, beginning with the most famous detective of all, Sherlock Holmes, and concluding with the adventures of a female wrestler.

crime fiction

About the text

Everybody has heard of Sherlock Holmes. In the nineteenth century, when these stories were published in magazines, they were enormously popular and even today, tourists search out Holmes' fictional address in Baker Street to pay their respects.

In this extract from *A Study in Scarlet*, you too can marvel at Holmes' powers of deduction. Holmes and his associate, Dr Watson have been summoned to the scene of a murder. Dr Watson takes up the story.

As you read, consider the following features of the text:

Word level

- Dr Watson, the narrator, comes across as rather slow-witted and always seems amazed by Holmes' abilities. Can you find some words or phrases that help create this impression?

- Holmes seems to be sarcastic and patronising towards the police. Can you find any words and phrases that create this impression?

Sentence level

- Look closely at the paragraph beginning, *As he spoke, he whipped a tape measure ...* on page 106. Notice how Arthur Conan Doyle makes Watson describe Holmes' actions. We are meant to follow his every movement so that we feel part of the investigation.

- How does Conan Doyle construct the sentences in this paragraph?

Text level

- Why do you think that Arthur Conan Doyle uses Watson to tell the stories rather than Holmes himself?

- Why do you think it is important for Dr Watson to be less clever than Holmes?

- Look at the end of the passage. How does Holmes humiliate the policemen?

A Study in Scarlet

by Arthur Conan Doyle

I had imagined that Sherlock Holmes would at once have hurried into the house and plunged into a study of the mystery. Nothing appeared to be further from his intention. With an air of **nonchalance** which, under the circumstances, seemed to me to border upon affectation, he lounged up and down the pavement, and gazed vacantly at the ground, the sky, the opposite houses and the line of railings. Having finished his scrutiny, he proceeded slowly down the path, or rather down the fringe of grass which flanked the path, keeping his eyes riveted upon the ground. Twice he stopped, and once I saw him smile, and heard him utter an exclamation of satisfaction. There were many marks of footsteps upon the wet clayey soil; but since the police had been coming and going over it, I was unable to see how my companion could hope to learn anything from it. Still, I had had such extraordinary evidence of the quickness of his perceptive **faculties**, that I had no doubt that he could see a great deal which was hidden from me.

At the door of the house we were met by a tall, white-faced, flaxen-haired man, with a notebook in his hand, who rushed forward and wrung my companion's hand with effusion. "It is indeed kind of you to come," he said, "I have had everything left untouched."

"Except that!" my friend answered, pointing at the pathway. "If a herd of buffaloes had passed along, there could not

nonchalance casual and relaxed behaviour

faculties mental or physical abilities

be a greater mess. No doubt, however, you had drawn your own conclusions, Gregson, before you permitted this."

"I have had so much to do inside the house," the detective said evasively. "My colleague, Mr. Lestrade, is here. I had relied upon him to look after this."

Holmes glanced at me and raised his eyebrows sardonically. "With two such men as yourself and Lestrade upon the ground, there will not be much for a third party to find out," he said.

Gregson rubbed his hands in a self-satisfied way. "I think we have done all that can be done," he answered; "it's a queer case, though, and I knew your taste for such things."

"You did not come here in a cab?" asked Sherlock Holmes.

"No, sir."

"Nor Lestrade?"

"No sir."

"Then let us go and look at the room." With which inconsequent remark he strode on into the house, followed by Gregson, whose features expressed his astonishment.

A short passage, bare-planked and dusty, led to the kitchen and offices. Two doors opened out of it to the left and to the right. One of these had obviously been closed for many weeks. The other belonged to the dining-room, which was the apartment in which the mysterious affair had occurred. Holmes walked in, and I followed him with that subdued feeling at my heart which the presence of death inspires.

It was a large square room, looking all the larger from the absence of furniture. A vulgar flaring paper adorned the walls, but it was blotched in places with mildew, and here and there great strips had become detached and hung down, exposing the yellow plaster beneath. Opposite the door was a showy fireplace, **surmounted** by a mantelpiece of imitation white marble. On one corner of this was stuck the stump of a red wax candle. The solitary window was so dirty that the light was hazy and uncertain, giving a dull grey tinge to everything, which was intensified by the thick layer of dust which coated the whole apartment.

All these details I observed afterwards. At present my attention was centred upon the single, grim, motionless figure which lay stretched upon the boards, with vacant, sightless eyes staring up at the discoloured ceiling. It was that of a man about forty-three or forty-four years of age, middle-sized, broad shouldered, with crisp curling black hair, and a short, stubbly beard. He was dressed in a heavy

surmounted capped, crowned

broadcloth frock coat and waistcoat, with light-coloured trousers, and immaculate collar and cuffs. A top hat, well brushed and trim, was placed upon the floor beside him. His hands were clenched and his arms thrown abroad, while his lower limbs were interlocked, as though his death struggle had been a grievous one. On his rigid face there stood an expression of horror, and, as it seemed to me, of hatred, such as I have never seen upon human features. This malignant and terrible contortion, combined with the low forehead, blunt nose, and **prognathous** jaw, gave the dead man a singularly **simious** and ape-like appearance, which was increased by his writhing, unnatural posture. I have seen death in many forms, but never has it appeared to me in a more fearsome aspect than in that dark, grimy apartment, which looked out upon one of the main arteries of suburban London.

Lestrade, lean and ferret-like as ever, was standing by the doorway, and greeted my companion and myself.

"This case will make a stir, sir," he remarked. "It beats anything I have seen, and I am no chicken."

"There is no clue?" said Gregson.

"None at all," chimed in Lestrade.

Sherlock Holmes approached the body, and, kneeling down, examined it intently. "You are sure that there is no wound?" he asked, pointing to numerous **gouts** and splashes of blood which lay all round.

"Positive!" cried both detectives.

"Then, of course, this blood belongs to a second individual – presumably the murderer, if murder has been committed. It reminds me of the circumstances attendant on the death of Van Jansen, in Utrecht, in the year '34. Do you remember the case, Gregson?"

"No, sir."

"Read it up – you really should. There is nothing new under the sun. It has all been done before."

As he spoke, his nimble fingers were flying here, there, and everywhere, feeling, pressing, unbuttoning, examining, while his eyes wore the same faraway expression which I have already remarked upon. So swiftly was the examination made, that one would hardly have guessed the minuteness with which it was conducted. Finally, he sniffed the dead man's lips, and then glanced at the soles of his patent leather boots.

"He has not been moved at all?" he asked.

"No more than was necessary for

prognathous	having a projecting jaw
simious	like an ape or monkey
gouts	splashes, spots

the purpose of our examination."

"You can take him to the mortuary now," he said. "There is nothing more to be learned."

Gregson had a stretcher and four men at hand. At his call they entered the room, and the stranger was lifted and carried out. As they raised him, a ring tinkled down and rolled across the floor. Lestrade grabbed it up and stared at it with mystified eyes.

"There's been a woman here," he cried. "It's a woman's wedding-ring."

He held it out, as he spoke, upon the palm of his hand. We all gathered round him and gazed at it. There could be no doubt that that circlet of plain gold had once adorned the finger of a bride.

"This complicates matters," said Gregson. "Heaven knows, they were complicated enough before."

"You're sure it doesn't simplify them?" observed Holmes. "There's nothing to be learned by staring at it. What did you find in his pockets?"

"We have it all here," said Gregson, pointing to a litter of objects upon one of the bottom steps of the stairs. "A gold watch, No. 97163, by Barraud of London. Gold Albert chain, very heavy and solid. Gold ring, with masonic device. Gold pin – bull-dog's head, with rubies as eyes. Russian leather card-case, with cards of Enoch J. Drebber of Cleveland, corresponding with the E. J. D. upon the linen. No purse, but loose money to the extent of seven pounds thirteen. Pocket edition of Boccaccio's 'Decameron', with name of Joseph Stangerson upon the fly-leaf. Two letters – one addressed to E. J. Drebber and one to Joseph Stangerson."

"At what address?"

"American Exchange, Strand – to be left till called for. They are both from the Guion Steamship Company, and refer to the sailing of their boats from Liverpool. It is clear that this unfortunate man was about to return to New York."

"Have you made any inquiries as to this man Stangerson?"

"I did it at once, sir," said Gregson. "I have had advertisements sent to all the newspapers, and one of my men has gone to the American Exchange, but he has not returned yet."

"Have you sent to Cleveland?"

"We telegraphed this morning."

"How did you word your inquiries?"

"We simply detailed the circumstances, and said that we should be glad of any information which could help us."

"You did not ask for particulars on any point which appeared to you to be crucial?"

"I asked about Stangerson."

"Nothing else? Is there no circumstance on which this whole case appears to hinge? Will you not telegraph again?"

"I have said all I have to say," said Gregson, in an offended voice.

Sherlock Holmes chuckled to himself, and appeared to be about to make some remark, when Lestrade, who had been in the front room while we were holding this conversation in the hall, reappeared upon the scene, rubbing his hands in a pompous and self-satisfied manner.

"Mr. Gregson," he said, "I have just made a discovery of the highest importance, and one which would have been overlooked had I not made a careful examination of the walls."

The little man's eyes sparkled as he spoke, and he was evidently in a state of suppressed exultation at having scored a point against his colleague.

"Come here," he said, bustling back into the room, the atmosphere of which felt clearer since the removal of its ghastly inmate. "Now, stand there!"

He struck a match on his boot and held it up against the wall.

"Look at that!" he said, triumphantly.

I have remarked that the paper had fallen away in parts. In this particular corner of the room a large piece had peeled off, leaving a yellow square of coarse plastering. Across this bare space there was scrawled in blood-red letters a single word:

RACHE

"What do you think of that?" cried the detective, with the air of a showman exhibiting his show. "This was overlooked because it was in the darkest corner of the room, and no one thought of looking there. The murderer has written it with his or her own blood. See this smear where it has trickled down the wall! That disposes of the idea of suicide anyhow. Why was that corner chosen to write it on? I will tell you. See that candle on the mantelpiece. It was lit at the time, and if it was lit this corner would be the brightest instead of the darkest portion of the wall."

deprecatory in a disparaging or belittling manner

"And what does it mean now that you *have* found it?" asked Gregson in a **deprecatory** voice.

"Mean? Why, it means that the writer was going to put the female name Rachel, but was disturbed before he or she had time to finish. You mark my words, when this case comes to be cleared up, you will find that a woman named Rachel has something to do with it. It's all very well for you to laugh, Mr Sherlock Holmes. You may be very smart and clever, but the old hound is the best, when all is said and done."

"I really beg your pardon!" said my companion, who had ruffled the little man's temper by bursting into an explosion of laughter. "You certainly have the credit of being the first of us to find this out and, as you say, it bears every mark of having been written by the other participant in last night's mystery. I have not had time to examine this room yet, but with your permission I shall do so now."

As he spoke, he whipped a tape measure and a large round magnifying glass from his pocket. With these two implements he trotted noiselessly about the room, sometimes stopping, occasionally kneeling, and once lying flat upon his face. So engrossed was he with his occupation that he appeared to have forgotten our presence, for he chattered away to himself under his breath the whole time, keeping up a running fire of exclamations, groans, whistles, and little cries suggestive of encouragement and of hope. As I watched him I was irresistibly reminded of a pureblooded, well-trained foxhound, as it dashes backwards and forwards through the **covert**, whining in its eagerness, until it comes across the lost scent. For twenty minutes or more he continued his researches, measuring with the most exact care the distance between marks which were entirely invisible to me, and occasionally applying his tape to the walls in an equally incomprehensible manner. In one place he gathered up very carefully a little pile of grey dust from the floor, and packed it away in an envelope. Finally, he examined with his glass the word upon the wall, going over every letter of it with the most minute exactness. This done, he appeared to be satisfied, for he replaced his tape and his glass in his pocket.

"They say that genius is an infinite capacity for taking pains," he remarked with a smile. "It's a very bad definition, but it does apply to detective work."

Gregson and Lestrade had watched the manœuvres of their amateur companion with considerable curiosity and some contempt. They evidently failed to appreciate the fact, which I had begun to realize, that Sherlock Holmes's smallest actions were all directed towards some definite and practical end.

covert thicket hiding game

"What do you think of it, sir?" they both asked.

"It would be robbing you of the credit of the case if I was to presume to help you," remarked my friend. "You are doing so well now that it would be a pity for anyone to interfere." There was a world of sarcasm in his voice as he spoke. "If you will let me know how your investigations go," he continued, "I shall be happy to give you any help I can. In the meantime I should like to speak to the constable who found the body. Can you give me his name and address?"

Lestrade glanced at his notebook. "John Rance," he said. "He is off duty now. You will find him at 46, Audley Court, Kennington Park Gate."

Holmes took a note of the address.

"Come along, Doctor," he said; "we shall go and look him up. I'll tell you one thing which may help you in the case," he continued, turning to the two detectives. "There has been murder done, and the murderer was a man. He was more than six feet high, was in the prime of life, had small feet for his height, wore coarse, square-toed boots and smoked a Trichinopoly cigar. He came here with his victim in a four-wheeled cab, which was drawn by a horse with three old shoes and one new one on his off foreleg. In all probability the murderer had a florid face, and the finger-nails of his right hand were remarkably long. These are only a few indications, but they may assist you."

Lestrade and Gregson glanced at each other with an incredulous smile.

"If this man was murdered, how was it done?" asked the former.

"Poison," said Sherlock Holmes curtly, and strode off. "One other thing, Lestrade," he added, turning round at the door: "'Rache' is the German for 'revenge'; so don't lose your time looking for Miss Rachel."

With which **Parthian shot** he walked away, leaving the two rivals open-mouthed behind him.

Parthian shot a shot fired in retreat

About the text

In the late 1930s a new kind of detective was born. Raymond Chandler and other writers such as Dashiell Hammett created a seedy world in which private eyes scratch a living in the violent cities of the US. This was in contrast with the more moral society (in which criminals were the exception) that Conan Doyle created. In Raymond Chandler's Los Angeles, 'everything you want belongs to somebody else, and the only way to get it is illegal, immoral, or deadly'.

In this extract from *The Big Sleep*, Chandler's detective, Philip Marlowe, has been beaten unconscious by gangsters working for a racketeer called Eddie Mars. Marlowe has been told that Mars's wife ran off with another man (Rusty Regan) but that Mars caught up with her and is holding her prisoner.

As you read, consider the following features of the text:

Word level

- Raymond Chandler uses a great deal of figurative language, especially similes and metaphors. What effect do these have?

Sentence level

- Look at the paragraph beginning, *She swung her head sharply...* on page 111. Note the way Raymond Chandler writes short, sharp sentences. This helps to maintain the tension. It also makes the writing read as if Marlowe is speaking directly to the reader.

Text level

- The writer often uses humour to bring his writing to life. Can you find some good examples?

- Look at the conversation between Marlowe and Mrs Mars. How would you describe it?

THE BIG SLEEP

by Raymond Chandler

IT SEEMED there was a woman and she was sitting near a lamp, which was where she belonged, in a good light. Another light shone hard on my face, so I closed my eyes again and tried to look at her through the lashes. She was so platinumed that her hair shone like a silver fruit bowl. She wore a green knitted dress with a broad white collar turned over it. There was a sharp-angled glossy bag at her feet. She was smoking and a glass of amber fluid was tall and pale at her elbow.

I moved my head a little, carefully. It hurt, but not more than I expected. I was trussed like a turkey ready for the oven. Handcuffs held my wrists behind me and a rope went from them to my ankles and then over the end of the brown **davenport** on which I was sprawled. The rope dropped out of sight over the davenport. I moved enough to make sure it was tied down.

I stopped these furtive movements and opened my eyes again and said: 'Hello.'

Lauren Bacall and
Humphrey Bogart in the
1946 film *The Big Sleep*

davenport large, heavily upholstered sofa (in USA)

The woman withdrew her gaze from some distant mountain peak. Her small firm chin turned slowly. Her eyes were the blue of mountain lakes. Overhead the rain still pounded, with a remote sound, as if it was somebody else's rain.

'How do you feel?' It was a smooth silvery voice that matched her hair. It had a tiny tinkle in it, like bells in a doll's house. I thought that was silly as soon as I thought of it.

'Great,' I said. 'Somebody built a filling station on my jaw.'

'What did you expect, Mr Marlowe — orchids?'

'Just a plain pine box,' I said. 'Don't bother with bronze or silver handles. And don't scatter my ashes over the blue Pacific. I like the worms better. Did you know that worms are of both sexes and that any worm can love any other worm?'

'You're a little light-headed,' she said, with a grave stare.

'Would you mind moving this light?'

She got up and went behind the davenport. The light went off. The dimness was a **benison**.

'I don't think you're so dangerous,' she said. She was tall rather than short, but no bean-pole. She was slim, but not a dried crust. She went back to her chair.

'So you know my name.'

'You slept well. They had plenty of time to go through your pockets. They did everything but embalm you. So you're a detective.'

'Is that all they have on me?'

She was silent. Smoke floated dimly from the cigarette. She moved it in the air. Her hand was small and had shape, not the usual bony garden tool you see on women nowadays.

'What time is it?' I asked.

She looked sideways at her wrist, beyond the spiral of smoke, at the edge of the grave lustre of the lamplight. 'Ten-seventeen. You have a date?'

'I wouldn't be surprised. Is this the house next to Art Huck's garage?'

'Yes.'

---

benison blessing

'What are the boys doing — digging a grave?'

'They had to go somewhere.'

'You mean they left you here alone?'

Her head turned slowly again. She smiled. 'You don't look dangerous.'

'I thought they were keeping you a prisoner.'

It didn't seem to startle her. It even slightly amused her. 'What made you think that?'

'I know who you are.'

Her very blue eyes flashed so sharply that I could almost see the sweep of their glance, like the sweep of a sword. Her mouth tightened. But her voice didn't change.

'Then I'm afraid you're in a bad spot. And I hate killing.'

'And you Eddie Mars's wife? Shame on you.'

She didn't like that. She glared at me. I grinned.

'Unless you can unlock these bracelets, which I'd advise you not to do, you might spare me a little of that drink you're neglecting.'

She brought the glass over. Bubbles rose in it like false hopes. She bent over me. Her breath was as delicate as the eyes of a fawn. I gulped from the glass. She took it away from my mouth and watched some of the liquid run down my neck.

She bent over me again. Blood began to move around in me, like a prospective tenant looking over a house.

'Your face looks like a collision mat,' she said.

'Make the most of it. It won't last long even this good.'

She swung her head sharply and listened. For an instant her face was pale. The sounds were only the rain drifting against the walls. She went back across the room and stood with her side to me, bent forward a little, looking down at the floor.

'Why did you come here and stick your neck out?' she asked quietly. 'Eddie wasn't doing you any harm. You know perfectly well that if I hadn't hid out here, the police would have been certain Eddie murdered Rusty Regan.'

'He did,' I said.

She didn't move, didn't change position an inch. Her breath made a harsh quick sound. I looked around the room. Two doors, both in the same wall, one half open.

A carpet of red and tan squares, blue curtains at the windows, a wallpaper with bright green pine trees on it. The furniture looked as if it had come from one of those places that advertise on bus benches. Gay, but full of resistance.

She said softly: 'Eddie didn't do anything to him. I haven't seen Rusty in months. Eddie's not that sort of man.'

'You left his bed and board. You were living alone. People at the place where you lived identified Regan's photo.'

'That's a lie,' she said coldly.

I tried to remember whether Captain Gregory had said that or not. My head was too fuzzy. I couldn't be sure.

'And it's none of your business,' she added.

'The whole thing is my business. I'm hired to find out.'

'Eddie's not that sort of man.'

'Oh, you like **racketeers**.'

'As long as people will gamble there will be places for them to gamble.'

'That's just protective thinking. Once outside the law you're all the way outside. You think he's just a gambler. I think he's a pornographer, a blackmailer, a hot car broker, a killer by remote control, and a **suborner** of crooked cops. He's whatever looks good to him, whatever has the cabbage pinned to it. Don't try to sell me on any high-souled racketeers. They don't come in that pattern.'

'He's not a killer.' She frowned.

'Not personally. He has Canino. Canino killed a man tonight, a harmless little guy who was trying to help somebody out. I almost saw him killed.'

She laughed wearily.

'All right,' I growled. 'Don't believe it. If Eddie is such a nice guy, I'd like to get to talk to him without Canino around. You know what Canino will do — beat my teeth out and then kick me in the stomach for mumbling.'

She put her head back and stood there thoughtful and

racketeer person who engages in dishonest and fraudulent business dealings

suborner someone who bribes or persuades others to commit crimes

crime fiction

withdrawn, thinking something out.

'I thought platinum hair was out of style,' I went on, just to keep sound alive in the room, just to keep from listening.

'It's a wig, silly. While mine grows out.' She reached up and yanked it off. Her own hair was clipped short all over, like a boy's. She put the wig back on.

'Who did that to you?'

She looked surprised. 'I had it done. Why?'

'Yes. Why?'

'Why, to show Eddie I was willing to do what he wanted me to do — hide out. That he didn't need to have me guarded. I wouldn't let him down. I love him.'

'Good grief,' I groaned. 'And you have me right here in the room with you.'

She turned a hand over and stared at it. Then abruptly she walked out of the room. She came back with a kitchen knife. She bent and sawed at my rope.

'Canino has the key to the handcuffs,' she said. 'I can't do anything about those.'

She stepped back, breathing rapidly. She had cut the rope at every knot.

'You're a kick,' she said. 'Kidding with every breath — the spot you're in.'

'I thought Eddie wasn't a killer.'

She turned away quickly and went back to her chair by the lamp and sat down and put her face in her hands. I swung my feet to the floor and stood up. I tottered around, stiff-legged. The nerve on the left side of my face was jumping in all its branches. I took a step. I could still walk. I could run, if I had to.

'I guess you mean me to go,' I said.

She nodded without lifting her head.

'You'd better go with me — if you want to keep on living.'

'Don't waste time. He'll be back any minute.'

'Light a cigarette for me.'

I stood beside her, touching her knees. She came to her feet with a sudden lurch. Our eyes were only inches apart.

'Hello, Silver-Wig,' I said softly.

About the text

Women have always written crime fiction but, until recently, their detectives tended to be rather genteel in comparison with the tough private eyes created by male writers. Nowadays, however, the female detectives can rough it out with the boys. Liza Cody's private eye, Eva Wylie (alias the *London Lassassin*, alias *Bucket Nut*) wants to be the Women's Heavyweight Wrestling Champion of Great Britain but, when she's not wrestling, she works as a security guard and does odd jobs for anyone who will pay her.

Eva has recently rescued a distraught young girl (Goldie) from a nightclub when it was raided by the police. The girl's boyfriend, Calvin, was singing in the club at the time. In this chapter, she is given a job by Mr Cheng, a restaurant owner and gangster.

Important note! Because of the nature of the passage, it is better to consider the following points **after** reading it. You might like to cover this box while you read.

Word level

- The language is colloquial. This gives the impression that we are listening to Eva tell her story. Can you find some examples?

Sentence level

- Look at the section from *The kitchen wall exploded...* to the end. What do you notice about the sentence structure in comparison with the earlier part of the chapter?

Text level

- Look at how Liza Cody increases our knowledge of Eva's character during this chapter.

- How does she make the explosion shocking and believable?

- Compare this extract with the extract from *The Big Sleep*. What are the similarities and differences?

Bucket Nut
by Liza Cody

'Listen to me, Eva,' said Auntie Lo. 'This is important.' She was alone in Mr Cheng's office, which was surprising because I hadn't seen Mr Cheng and the other two come out.

   'Where's Mr Cheng?' I asked.

   'Eva!' said Auntie Lo. 'You must listen.'

   'OK.' But I was puzzled because I couldn't see a door except the one I had used.

   'This is a very important little job,' she said. 'It's because Kenny is in hospital. If not, he would do it. See?'

   'Yeah.' I did feel bad about Kenny. The nurse in Casualty told me he had several cracked ribs, and I think she said he had a bruised lung, but I couldn't be quite sure. Anyway it sounded painful.

'It wasn't my fault,' I said.

'Don't you want to help Mr Cheng?' Auntie Lo asked. She looked so Auntyish in her pleated skirt and grey woolly. I looked at her feet and sure enough she was wearing pink dancing shoes.

'Of course I want to help,' I said.

'Good,' she said. 'Mr Cheng wants you to deliver a package.'

'OK.'

'It is important. It is important that nobody sees. For your protection.'

'Mine?' I said. Auntie Lo was not smiling, and I wished she would make her joke about finding me a husband instead of talking about how important it all was.

'I like you, Eva,' she said. 'Mr Cheng trusts you. We do not wish to get you into trouble.'

'I don't mind a bit of trouble.' I suddenly felt very happy.

'We mind. So you must be careful. The package is for Mr Aycliffe. He is expecting it. But there are two things.' She held up two fingers. 'Two important things. One – you must not be seen giving it to him. Two – you must not see his face.

'Why?'

'Mr Aycliffe is being watched by the police. They wish to catch him and put him in prison. We do not want this to happen. Mr Aycliffe is a good man who has made some mistakes but he does not deserve prison. This arrangement will protect you, and it will protect Mr Aycliffe.'

'Oh,' I said. She gave me a moment to think about it. Then I said, 'How can I give Mr Aycliffe a package if I can't see him?'

'We have thought a lot about this, Eva. And we have a plan. Mr Aycliffe works at a club near the Harrow Road. You know the Harrow Road, Eva?'

'Yeah.'

'There is a front entrance – which you do *not* use. You do not use front door, Eva, Right?'

'Right.'

'You use kitchen door.'

'Kitchen door. Right.'

'The door will open, but there won't be anyone in the kitchen.'

'How do you know there won't be anyone in the kitchen?'

Auntie Lo looked at her watch. 'Too late,' she said. 'Kitchen closed. Only drinks served from bar. Mr Aycliffe has told us this.'

I should have thought of that. By most people's reckoning it was nearly morning. Late night clubs were different.

'This package,' Auntie Lo went one, 'is in a Safeway carrier bag. To look like rubbish, Eva. You walk into kitchen. You will see another door. Through that door is passage. In passage is where they put the empties. All crates, bottles, other rubbish. You put the Safeway bag with this other rubbish, Eva. You got that?'

'Yeah.'

'Then you walk out. When club closes it is Mr Aycliffe's job to take out rubbish. See?'

'Oh, I get it,' I said. 'He takes out the rubbish and takes the package at the same time. And no one will know a thing about it.'

'That is correct. I see you got brains too, Eva. Not just a pretty face.' Auntie Lo suddenly started her huff-huff laughter. And that made me laugh too. It was one of her jokes. I know for a fact that neither Auntie Lo nor Mr Cheng think I'm very smart. It's because they are Chinese, and as everyone knows Chinese people are very smart indeed.

So I didn't mind very much when Auntie Lo went through all her instructions again. She practically drew me a map of how to get to the kitchen of Mr Aycliffe's place. Then she let me go.

It was a funny time of night – not many people in the streets. Just one or two rolling home, one or two still looking for somewhere to score and one or two off to work on the early shift. Normally I like being out and about when it's halfway between late and early. But this time I was a bit strung out. I was worried about Goldie and I was worried about Auntie Lo's package. Also, I was being followed. I drove in the VW but I noticed two Chinese blokes not far behind in Mr Cheng's Rover.

It was just like Mr Cheng to give me a job and then send someone along to make sure I did it right. But it made me tense all the same.

Mostly, when people give you instructions about how to get somewhere they make a mistake or they leave something out. Auntie Lo made no mistakes and she left nothing out. That's how smart she is – everything was exactly the way she said it would be.

The place looked like a **shebeen** from the front. It was in a broken down row of buildings and there was music coming from the open door. I drove past and turned the corner.

The kitchen door was old and wooden, but it was covered with locks and bolts. The back street looked as if it needed all the locks and bolts you could throw at it. There were broken windows and doors with kicked in panels and houses I knew without looking were filled with dossers.

But inside the kitchen it smelled of onions and chillies and it wasn't all that dirty even though they had left a lot of washing up in the sink.

The music was very loud so nobody could have heard me come in. I went over to the door opposite and opened

shebeen unlicensed house selling alcohol

it slowly. The passage was just what I was expecting. It wasn't lit, but coloured lights spilled through the doors to the bar and dance floor. I saw all the empty bottles and crates stacked to one side. I put the Safeway carrier bag on top of them.

I should have left straight away but I couldn't resist having a gander through the bar door to see if I could spot Mr Aycliffe.

I pushed the door open just a crack. The music was deafening. At first all I could see was a few people dancing and a few people drinking. And then I noticed that one of the dancers was Calvin. Goldie's lover boy, the Lord of the Trousers. He was dancing with an absolutely gorgeous lady. She looked totally wigged-out and she was hanging round his neck like a garland of flowers, but you could see from the shape of her and the way the other men watched her that she was absolutely gorgeous.

Poor Goldie. It made me want to hang the bleeding snotgobbler from the light bulb and swing on his feet. I mean, what right did a little turd like that

crime fiction

have to mess with a nice woman's affections? Especially when she was a friend of mine.

Another time I might have steamed in and sorted him out. But now I was under orders to be invisible – although why anyone would pick me up for that when I'm one of the most visible women I know, was a mystery. When I thought about it I realised that, of course, it wasn't me they'd picked. They had picked Kenny. And Kenny, if my experience of not seeing him was anything to go by, was about as visible as the Holy Ghost.

I sneaked a last quick look at Calvin and his luscious lady. If he was a woman, I thought, they'd probably call him a slag. As it was they would call her a slag and him a stud and it just wasn't fair. All that man-woman stuff really gets up my nose. I'm glad I'm not involved.

Leaving the music and the coloured lights behind I crossed the passage and went back into the kitchen. It was time to make a quick exit. But when I got to the kitchen door I found I couldn't open it.

I pushed, and I rattled the handle, and I put my shoulder to it but the door was stuck fast.

'S**t a bus,' I said out loud. Because if I couldn't get through the kitchen door I would have to go out through the bar and then everyone would see me – including Calvin who might recognise me from Bermuda Smith's club. And then Mr Cheng and Auntie Lo would be peeved and perhaps they wouldn't give me any more work. You have to do what you are told and be reliable or they don't trust you.

There was one small window, but there were bars across it. The bars wouldn't budge an inch when I heaved on them. The only hope was the door.

I went back to it and tried again. I hauled up on the handle in case the bottom was jammed. It wasn't.

I was sweating like live pork in a sauna. I couldn't understand what was happening. The door had opened so easily when I went in. Everything had gone according to plan. How could such a cock-up happen at the last minute?

It was stupid. It was only a door.

I backed away. Took a run. And hit the door near the lock with a drop-kick. This was a dodgy move. With flying kicks you can land on your arse if you get it wrong. But I heard something splinter.

I picked myself up and tried the handle again. This time it felt looser.

I backed off again and took a longer run. I hit the door perfectly just below the handle. There was a tearing sound of rotten wood splitting, and the door popped open. Thank the Lord for a good pair of boots.

Outside, I closed the door as best I could. And … well … it is hard to describe what happened next. It was like a dream.

You see, I had just found out why the door wouldn't open, when this thing happened.

The kitchen wall exploded.

It did.

It just flew outwards. One minute it was a wall, and the next minute it was bricks and mortar flying through the air.

The door fell on me.

I remember thinking what a waste of effort it was kicking it open, when it was going to fall over anyway.

I swear I didn't black out, but when I opened my eyes, both me and the door were in the middle of the road yards away from the kitchen and I couldn't remember how we got there.

The funny thing was that I did not hear a thing.

I just saw the wall come apart. And the door fell on me. That's all.

It was like a dream.

It was so weird I actually thought I *was* dreaming. Really dreaming.

You know those dreams where you have to get home? You *must* get home but you don't know the way because you don't know where you are now.

Well it was like that.

I got up. There was rubble all over the street. There were flames and smoke. There were one or two people moving very slowly.

I walked away. I thought, 'I'm dreaming about the war.'

I remember seeing a car bent in half. And another one with a table poking through the windscreen.

But I just walked away because I thought I was dreaming about the war and I had to get home. I couldn't hear anything, so it had to be a dream. Right?

I just sort of floated away. I couldn't hear anything and I couldn't feel anything. I couldn't even feel my own feet on the pavement. That is what dreams are like.

There was a woman in the gutter, stark naked and covered in blood. She had bits of glass sticking out of her skin. Her mouth was wide open, as if she was screaming. But I couldn't hear her so I floated on by.

Because it was a dream, see, a dream about the war, and I had to go home.